CLOSED-CIRCUIT
TELEVISION
Handbook

To My Wife, Dorothy,

For Her Unending Patience and Understanding

CLOSED-CIRCUIT TELEVISION

Handbook

by LEON A. WORTMAN

HOWARD W. SAMS & CO., INC.
THE BOBBS-MERRILL CO., INC.
INDIANAPOLIS · KANSAS CITY · NEW YORK

SECOND EDITION

FIRST PRINTING—1969

Library of Congress Catalog Card Number: 71-92465

Preface

Much has been written about the technical history of television and how it was born; however, there appears to be very little about *why* it was born. Ask people why, in their opinion, television was invented, and the majority, without hesitation, will answer for home entertainment. Television is much more than a medium for entertainment; it is invaluable in education, industry, the sciences, research, and the military services.

Until now, however, little written material has been available on closed-circuit television systems. Most people know that this type of TV system exists, a few probably realize that there are far more closed-circuit installations than broadcast stations, but little else is known.

As is pointed out in this book, although TV equipment is often quite complex, you do not have to be an engineer to understand it and enjoy its benefits. To become proficient in its use you do not have to learn a new trade; also, unlimited financial resources are not necessary to own a closed-circuit TV system. By giving specifics, I hope to assist many who are wondering about the feasibility of CCTV in their own situations. Furthermore, I hope those who are now making systems and equipment decisions will find authoritative guidance in this book.

The following text takes you from the basic concepts of closed-circuit television systems and equipment to the more complex aspects. The book progresses through the diverse applications. Hard-to-find information on the vitally important practical subjects of lighting and optics for television is given. Finally, circuit descriptions are included for the more technical reader who may be responsible for service and maintenance.

You can start reading this book from front to back, chapter by chapter, or you can select only those chapters whose titles indicate immediate interest. Either way, I believe there is material of interest to all who want to learn more about the fascinating subject of closed-circuit television.

As with any "handbook," this book could not have been written without the cooperation of those who design, develop, manufacture, market, service, and operate closed-circuit television equipment. My sincere thanks go to the many who assisted in the compilation of the material used in preparing this book.

LEON A. WORTMAN

Contents

CHAPTER 7

CHAPTER 8

CHAPTER 9

CHAPTER 10

CHAPTER 11

What Is Closed-Circuit Television?

ALL TELEVISION SYSTEMS have several things in common. This is true no matter where or for what purpose they are used, and no matter who the audience is or what the subject being televised is. All systems use television cameras to "photograph" the subject, and they all use television receivers to show the "photograph" to the audience. In addition, at least one of the several possible methods of connecting the camera and receiver is employed in every system.

The general public is most familiar with the method used by commercial-TV broadcast stations to bring programs to the home viewer. In this system the TV station uses a transmitter which basically has a television camera at its input and an antenna at its output. The transmitter generates energy that is modified (modulated) by the camera so that it varies in accordance with the scene being televised. This varying energy (called the signal) is radiated into the atmosphere by the antenna. Then the antenna at the home viewer's television receiver picks up some of the radiated energy. This energy is amplified and converted inside the television receiver to become a reproduction of the scene being "photographed" by the television camera.

In Fig. 1-1 a cable is used to connect the camera with the receiver. When a cable connection is between the camera and receiver the method is called closed-circuit television. The camera, cable, receiver, and any other components that might be used to televise a scene are all part of the system. If we substitute the word "private" for "closed," we have an effective, though possibly oversimplified, definition of a closed-circuit television system.

In closed-circuit television, programs or pictures are sent to specified locations for specific individuals or groups. When television pictures or programs are broadcast in a generally nondirectional pattern and are made available without special fees to all who have conventional TV sets, the system is not considered to be closed. Such a system is completely "unprivate" and is referred to as "open circuit."

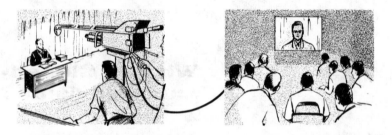

Fig. 1-1. The basic closed-circuit television system using a cable to connect the TV camera at the studio (left) and the TV receiver at the viewing room (right).

Sometimes the generality is made that closed-circuit television uses coaxial cables to interconnect all elements of the system. The term "direct-wire television" is, in fact, used by some equipment manufacturers to describe closed-circuit TV cameras and monitors. This has reinforced the impression that a closed-circuit television system *necessarily* uses cables throughout the system. At one time in the development of techniques this was true. Cables provided the only practical means for maintaining continuity between the camera and the viewer in a closed circuit; however, it is now quite practicable to eliminate coaxial cable interconnections when the originating and viewing locations are inconveniently located with respect to each other. This can be done without losing the characteristic of privacy that is inherent in a closed-circuit television system. Special radio links (Fig. 1-2) provide the connection between the two points.

Extraordinary advances in technology and significant breakthroughs in the simplification of equipment have made private radio relay systems feasible for users of closed-circuit television. Such radio relay systems are licensed by the Federal Communications Commission, Washington, D.C. They are designed for operation at microwave frequencies from approximately 1.9 Gc (1,900,000,000 cycles per second) to 13 Gc.

One of the characteristics of microwave signals is that they can be focused into an extremely narrow beam. In addition, microwave signals tend to travel in a straight line, as does a light beam. They do not bend, turn, or curve around opaque objects. Light beams can be redirected by placing a reflective object in their path. Likewise, by using special reflective devices, microwave radio beams can be redirected to a desired

Fig. 1-2. A closed-circuit system in which the TV camera and the receiver are connected via a microwave radio relay.

location. The narrowness of the beam dispersion angle is not affected by reflective devices. The angle of the beam is so narrow that the signal traveling from the transmitting antenna to the receiving antenna cannot be intercepted without interrupting the beam. Transmission thus remains private, and therefore closed to unauthorized equipment.

Electrical impulses from a television camera can be used to modulate the signal broadcast by a microwave transmitter, and a microwave receiver can be used to feed the modulated signals to a television monitor. Thus pictures can be sent from one location to another without coaxial cables and still be a closed-circuit system.

A complete understanding of the differences between closed and open circuits will prevent confusion in comprehending the utility of the many types of systems available. For example, there are television systems that combine open and closed techniques. In this system, commercially-broadcast TV programs are made available to homes located beyond the useful range of TV transmitters.

In many areas which are deprived of conventional TV reception because of geography, privately operated companies have found it profitable to install towers, TV antennas, and specially designed receiving equipment to enable reception of usable television signals. These signals are amplified and fed into coaxial cables. The cables are usually strung along telephone-type poles through the streets of the area being serviced. Home-

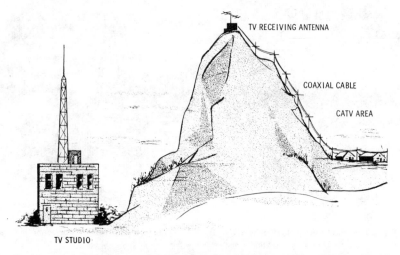

Fig. 1-3. A community antenna (CATV) system. The signal is received at the mountain top and sent down the mountain side over coaxial cable.

owners make arrangements to rent a connection to the coaxial cable, similar to the way a telephone connection is rented, at a monthly or period rate. Homeowners provide their own television sets, which are tuned in the conventional manner. No roof-top or indoor antenna is needed. Only those sets connected to the coaxial cable are able to receive the programs. This interesting combination of "open" and "closed" circuits, known as *Community Antenna Television* (CATV), is illustrated in Fig. 1-3. In 1963 more than 1,000 communities in the United States were being regularly serviced by CATV installations.

The basic meaning of closed-circuit systems should be evident from the foregoing. A closed-circuit television (CCTV) system is intended to provide privacy, regardless of the method used to interconnect cameras and monitors. As long as it is not practicable for unauthorized monitors to intercept and reproduce the pictures being transmitted from the cameras, it is a closed-circuit television system.

In the chapters that follow, you will be concerned with CCTV equipment and systems to the exclusion of CATV and commercial-TV broadcast operations.

APPLICATIONS

Closed-circuit television systems are being used in many different ways. Frequently the daily press reports the use of closed-circuit TV in conjunction with major sports events. In such instances TV rights may be sold to promotion groups who then lease theaters throughout the country for the duration of the event. The theaters are then linked to where the sports event originates by coaxial cable and/or microwave links. Cameras are installed at the event and large-screen TV projectors are installed at the theaters. Theater seats are sold to the general public, thus enabling them to be spectators, even though they are thousands of miles away.

Salespeople are becoming increasingly familiar with closed-circuit television. Many have seen it at work during sales conferences. Closed-circuit systems have made it possible for executive officers to speak to the "conference" despite the fact that they are physically unable to attend. Often, when it is not practical to call the entire sales force in to the main office to unveil a new line of products, theaters are rented across the country (Fig. 1-4). The salesmen then assemble at these points to see the new models and learn about their features.

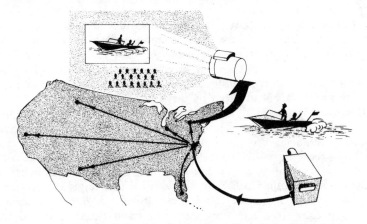

Fig. 1-4. Use of closed-circuit television during sales meetings.

Industry, science, and research groups have found TV cameras and monitors to be invaluable. At times TV makes it possible to perform functions that would otherwise not be practical. In Fig. 1-5 a dangerous radioactive process is being performed. The operator can manipulate the mechanical robot behind the safety of a solid wall and perform the entire operation. The TV camera and receiver enable him to view the entire operation. In other applications CCTV has increased the efficiency of many operations and improved the reliability of automated machinery

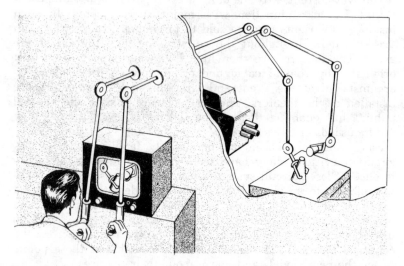

Fig. 1-5. A dangerous radioactive process being performed using mechanical hands and closed-circuit television.

by providing a constant visual observation. In plant security applications, CCTV is used to provide visual surveillance of entrances and work areas. Guards can view all areas from one control point and sound the alarm when there is a security violation. Such a system provides better security at less risk to personnel, and it is not affected by adverse weather.

Probably the most dynamic area of growth for closed-circuit television systems has been in education. TV cameras have greatly advanced the level of instruction in many schools by enabling teachers with special skills to reach numbers of students who would otherwise be inaccessible. Educational television systems have helped alleviate the critical shortages of teaching personnel and upgraded the literacy levels in deprived areas. In many cases, the learning processes have been enhanced by the improvement in teaching techniques. For instance, in Fig. 1-6

Fig. 1-6. A TV camera focused through a microscope so the entire class can view the enlarged picture while seated.

the biology instructor is using a TV camera focused through the eyepiece of a microscope to give an enlarged view of the slide to the entire class. The entire class can see the slide simultaneously while seated. Thus, much time that would be wasted during individual viewings is saved.

In commerce, closed-circuit television systems have made significant contributions to efficiency and profitability of business. CCTV systems have become invaluable communication tools where visual data must be transferred or observed; they have eliminated geography as a barrier to "doing business."

SYSTEM PLANNING

Proper planning of a closed-circuit television system requires a practical understanding of equipment, and a realistic appraisal of the requirements of the application. There are many manufacturers of equipment from which you can select units. The cameras, monitors, and accessories they produce may vary considerably in performance, quality, physical dimensions, controls, conveniences, and costs. A high-cost TV camera designed especially for nuclear research could be totally inadequate in an educational television situation. Conversely, the educational-TV camera would not be satisfactory in the nuclear-research application. A camera that performs perfectly indoors under regulated lighting conditions may be almost useless at an outdoor sports event.

Fortunately you do not have to become an electronics engineer to intelligently plan a system or to develop specifications for major units of equipment in a given application. However, it is impossible to plan or specify without a working knowledge of some of the fundamentals of television equipment and systems and without a good comprehension of the vocabulary used in the field of closed-circuit television. A familiarity with the capabilities and limitations of specific cameras, monitors, and auxiliary equipment is also necessary before the systems planner can function.

Experiences with closed-circuit television practices have enabled the establishment of reliable "ground rules" where considerations cannot be reduced to technical data. Where available, performance factors, definitions, data, and standards of good practice are given throughout this book. It is this type of information that the "old timers" in closed-circuit television systems planning, installation, and operation use to compare equipment capabilities with the intended application. It is as important to thoroughly understand the requirements of your own application as it is to understand the proposed equipment.

Simple Systems

The simplest type of closed-circuit television system is diagrammed in Fig. 1-7. This system consists of two units of equipment, a television camera and a television receiver. The camera and the receiver are connected by a two-conductor wire called a *coaxial cable.*

The camera detects, or picks up, light that is reflected from the scene to be televised. Inside the camera these impressions of light are converted to electrical signals that vary in intensity in a direct relationship to the intensity of the light. The electrical signals are fed through the coaxial cable to the television receiver. The receiver then reconverts the electrical signals back to light values, reproducing the original scene on the face of the picture tube.

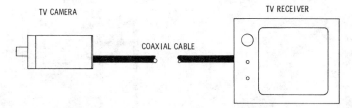

Fig. 1-7. The basic closed-circuit television system.

In practice, the system of Fig. 1-7 can be expected to provide useful picture pickup and reproduction with a maximum of 1,000 feet of cable between the camera and the monitor. This is true if all the equipment is in optimum operating condition and scene lighting is proper.

A coaxial cable consists of two conductors, one completely encircling the other for their entire lengths (Fig. 1-8). The outer conductor is usually a network of wires braided into a tube-like form. A solid-copper wire is used for the inner conductor. The two conductors are separated from each other by an insulating material known as a dielectric. Because the braided-wire outer conductor completely encircles the inner conductor, it functions as an "interference shield" as well as a conductor. In most cables this outer conductor is covered by a protective plastic cover to prevent damage to the conductors. The outside diameter of the cable is usually from ¼ to ½ inch.

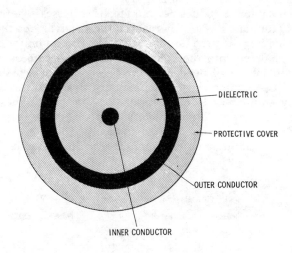

Fig. 1-8. Cross-sectional view of coaxial cable.

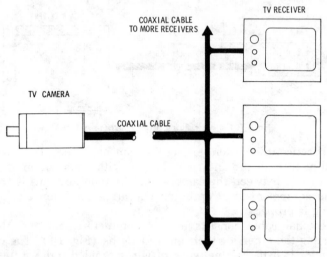

Fig. 1-9. A large number of TV receivers connected to a coaxial cable.

Complex Systems—Several Receivers

It is a relatively simple matter to add more television receivers to the simple system of Fig. 1-7. (This is shown in Fig. 1-9.) A few simple rules have to be observed, however. When the monitors are widely dispersed from each other, or when all or any one of them is a significant distance from the camera location, the system becomes less simple.

Coaxial cables introduce certain electrical losses. Therefore the signal is attenuated before it reaches the receiver. As the length of the cable increases, so do the losses. Depending on the strength of the signal fed into the coaxial cable at the camera end and the amount of signal needed at the receiver end to assure good pictures, it sometimes becomes necessary to make provisions for accessory equipment to compensate for the losses. These accessories are known as *line amplifiers* simply because they amplify the electricity that is on the line connecting the camera and the monitors. The addition of a line amplifier is illustrated in Fig. 1-10.

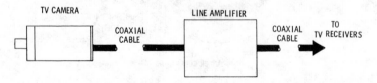

Fig. 1-10. Addition of a line amplifier to the system to amplify the signals in the cable.

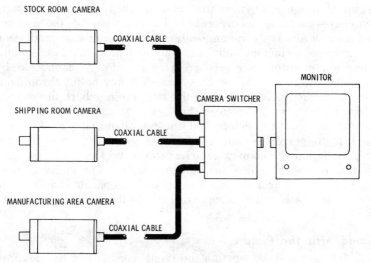

Fig. 1-11. A system using three cameras and a single monitor.

Complex Systems—Several Cameras

Frequently the requirements of an application include the use of several cameras with one or more monitors. When the cameras are all in operation at the same time, each is connected to an individual monitor for simultaneous viewing and surveillance; hence the system is in reality nothing more than a group of *simple* systems. However, when the requirements specify that each of the several cameras must be selected at will to feed one

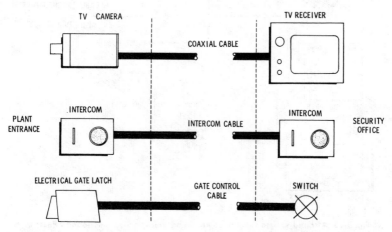

Fig. 1-12. An office-type intercom added to a simple closed-circuit TV installation.

group of monitors, a new unit of equipment—called a camera switcher—must be incorporated. The location of the camera switcher varies with the application. For example, a production manager in a factory may be equipped with a closed-circuit television monitor in his office. This monitor is connected by coaxial cable to several cameras located at key points throughout the plant. Such points might be the stockroom, where the camera is focused on an inventory sheet; the shipping room, where bottlenecks might develop; and the manufacturing area, where hazards to personnel might otherwise go undetected. In such an installation the camera switcher would be located in the production manager's office, beside the monitor. The manager then has complete control of camera selection. A separate coaxial cable is run from each of the cameras directly to the switcher, as shown in Fig. 1-11.

Sound with the Picture

A "picture may be worth a thousand words," but telecasts are incomplete when no provision is made for making the words

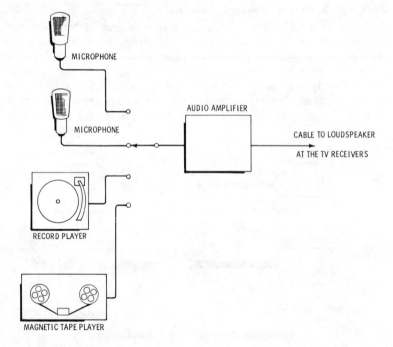

Fig. 1-13. A sound system capable of providing voice, music, and sound effects in conjunction with closed-circuit television.

audible to the viewer. As with the picture system, the sound system can be quite simple; no more than an office-type intercom may be needed in a simple setup. For example, a camera installed at a gate to a factory (Fig. 1-12) may be used to visually identify a person seeking entrance. A conventional intercom enables the security officer observing the television screen to carry on a two-way conversation with the person. Usually, such a remotely observed gate is locked and unlocked electrically by the guard at the TV-observation point. In effect, the picture and the sound systems as well as the gate latch are entirely separate from each other (Fig. 1-12).

A more complex sound system might contain means for feeding audio from a magnetic tape reproducer, a record player, and several microphones. The system might have the capability of feeding the audio sources one at a time, or simultaneously. The capability of feeding from simultaneous sources makes it practical to play background music during a dramatic reading, or to add recorded sound effects (or music) to theatrical performances. This capability is extremely desirable in any installation intended for use in an educational or instructional television service. Fig. 1-13 shows a sound system suited for studio-type telecasts. Special techniques for getting the sound from the location at the camera to the location of the viewer will be detailed later in this book.

Cameras

THE NECESSARY COMPONENTS for any type of television system are a camera, a receiver, and a method for interconnecting the two. As was pointed out in Chapter 1, the interconnection may be by coaxial cable or by radio relay. The function of the camera is to optically detect a scene, convert the optical information into a sequence of electrical impulses, and feed those impulses to a terminal. When the terminal is a TV receiver, the electrical impulses are used to reproduce the scene on which the camera is focused.

VIDICONS AND IMAGE ORTHICONS

The two types of cameras most frequently used in closed-circuit television are the *image orthicon* and the *vidicon*. These names are taken from the type of picture pickup tubes the cameras use. The vidicon tube (Fig. 2-1), which forms the heart of operation of a vidicon camera, is only 6½ inches long and 1 inch in diameter. The tube's compact size, good durability, relatively low cost, and long life make it possible to develop cameras small enough, inexpensive enough, and simple enough in operation for use by nonprofessionals.

A brief comparison with the image orthicon camera will show why the vidicon, developed in the early 1950's, quickly became the answer to a wide variety of television needs outside of commercial broadcasting.

The price of vidicon cameras ranges from approximately $400 to $5,000. Image orthicon cameras are in the $20,000-up category. The image orthicon tube (Fig. 2-2) may be either 3 or 4½ inches in diameter; its overall size and complexity demand professionally trained personnel. Professional 35-mm lenses are required for image orthicon cameras, while vidicon cameras use relatively less expensive universally available 16-mm lenses.

Not only is the vidicon tube less expensive to replace (about 1/10 the cost of an image orthicon), but its life expectancy is about 5 times greater than that of the image orthicon. This makes the cost comparisons on a cost-per-hour-of-operation basis move dramatically in favor of the vidicon camera.

The scale of values is not all one-sided, however. As a live program pickup, the image orthicon is far more sensitive. In addition, it surpasses the vidicon in other areas of concern to commercial broadcast television stations. Experience has shown that for most nonbroadcast applications, however, the vidicon TV camera is adequate. Therefore it is widely used in closed-circuit television applications.

The choice of vidicon cameras is quite broad, and, given reasonable care, the vidicon tube is quite durable. Extremely little train-

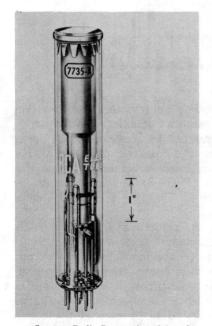

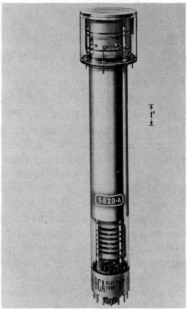

Courtesy Radio Corporation of America

Fig. 2-1. The vidicon camera tube.

Courtesy Radio Corporation of America

Fig. 2-2. An image orthicon camera tube.

ing is needed for operators of vidicon cameras to become proficient. In fact, many vidicon cameras are as easy to operate as a conventional home television receiver.

Since the vidicon camera is the first choice for most closed-circuit television systems, the remainder of this chapter is devoted to this type.

TYPES OF VIDICON CAMERAS

Two types of vidicon cameras are in popular use. The differences are not in the vidicons, but in the nature of the output signal supplied by the camera to the coaxial cable. Their identifying labels are *RF camera* and *VF camera*. Each offers combinations of advantages and disadvantages which are readily understood. Again, by comparison of the requirements for a specific application with the merits of the two camera types, one can make the right choice.

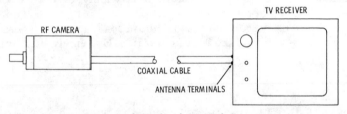

Fig. 2-3. A simple RF closed-circuit television system.

RF System

The letters "RF" are the popular abbreviation for the term *radio frequency*. Thus, an RF camera contains radio-frequency impulses similar to those transmitted by a commercial "open-circuit" television station. Because of this, the output of an RF camera can be connected directly to the antenna terminals of a conventional home television set (Fig. 2-3). No circuit modification of the television set is required. This type of overall system is referred to as an *RF system*.

It is common practice to design RF cameras so that their signals can be tuned in on Channels 2 through 6. A choice of channels is necessary so that the user can operate the camera on an unoccupied TV channel. Otherwise, interference from a commercial-TV broadcast station would result. Channels 2 through 6 are at the low-frequency end of the spectrum assigned for commercial telecasting. RF cameras are designed to operate at the lower frequencies because the camera (and all other units within the system) will operate more efficiently at these frequencies.

Some RF cameras may be continuously tuned from Channels 2 through 6. This is an advantage, if the camera is to be moved geographically, because the operator can tune to a clear channel each time he sets up his equipment. If the equipment or the system is to be operated at the same location, the tunability provision is of little value.

A number of cameras are equipped for single-channel or fixed-tuned RF output. The desired TV channel of operation should be predetermined in the planning stages of the system and specified when ordering the camera. Should it become necessary to change the operating channel, modifications can be easily made in the field. Usually only the changing of a plug-in oscillator crystal and realigning a tuned circuit within the camera are involved. No special test equipment is necessary. Any person who is technically qualified may make the adjustments; no FCC license is required.

The output signal of an RF camera contains four types of electrical impulses—horizontal synchronizing, vertical synchronizing, video, and radio frequency. All of these are essential to the correct operation of an RF system. The specific function of each of the signals is detailed in a later chapter.

VF System

The letters "VF" are the popular abbreviation for the term *video frequency*. This designates the type of signal supplied to the system from the camera output. The output signal of a VF camera contains the first three of the four types of electrical impulses contained in the RF-camera output signal. A VF camera does not contain radio-frequency circuitry; therefore it cannot be connected directly to the antenna terminals of a conventional TV set. Either the TV set must be modified (jeeped), or a special video monitor must be used in conjunction with a VF camera. A simple VF system is diagramed in Fig. 2-4.

Just as a monitor for an RF camera cannot be used directly with a VF camera, a VF monitor cannot be used directly with an RF camera. They are not interchangeable without modification or special attachments. A VF monitor has no circuitry for tuning

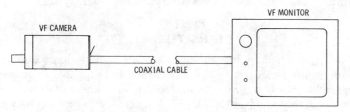

Fig. 2-4. A simple VF closed-circuit television system.

to the commercial-TV channels and no built-in sound amplifier or speaker.

CAMERA CONTROLS

Everyone is familiar with the fact that home-type TV sets are equipped with controls for channel selection and varying the brightness and contrast. These controls, which are referred to as primary controls, are usually fitted with knobs and located for convenient manipulation. Other controls, such as the focus, vertical and horizontal hold, height, and linearity controls, are usually at the rear of the TV set and are not normally adjusted by the viewer. They are known as the secondary controls. Monitors designed especially for closed-circuit television applications have the same controls and perform the same functions as those in the home-TV set.

RF and VF cameras are also equipped with primary and secondary controls. They have the same effect on the picture as the controls at the TV monitor. An immediate conclusion that one can draw is that if one can control contrast, for example, at both ends of the system, a considerable range of adjustment is feasible. Thus, it is possible to provide considerable compensation in brilliance and contrast for a poorly illuminated scene. This does not mean that a poorly illuminated scene can be resolved into a good picture. It does mean that if it is important to achieve high degrees of contrast from a relatively monotonous scene without regard to detail or sharpness, it can be done.

Often it will appear that the scene on the monitor screen is brighter than the original scene being televised. This appears to be so because of the increased contrast. This increased contrast is especially useful in applications where an area is to be observed—for example, in surveillance work where detection of motion is essential but positive identification of the moving body is not. When it is essential to read data or to make precise identification, there is no complete compensation for a poorly illuminated scene. Proper lighting is one of the factors required for optimum operation of any closed-circuit television system.

LENS TURRET

The camera in Fig. 2-5 is equipped with a single lens. Standard 16-mm motion-picture lenses are used. In Fig. 2-5 a general-purpose 25-mm f1.9 lens is mounted on the camera. Lens turrets are also widely used in CCTV. With a lens turret more than one lens is mounted on the camera. Fig. 2-6 shows a camera with

Courtesy Fairchild Camera & Equipment Corp.

Fig. 2-5. A single-lens closed-circuit television system.

three lenses mounted on the turret. Selection of the lens best suited to the field of view is made by rotating the turret and placing the desired lens in an operating position as in photography. A wide-angle lens, a normal-field lens, and a telephoto lens, for instance, can be mounted on the turret.

There are several methods by which the turret is rotated. Some are manual; others are mechanical or electromechanical, depending on the individual camera. With a manual turret, the operator grasps the turret and turns it to place the desired lens in the operating position. The mechanical technique usually includes a knob, handle, or lever which is located at the rear of the camera housing and is mechanically linked or geared to the turret for

Courtesy Sylvania Electric Products, Inc.

Fig. 2-6. The Sylvania Model 600 camera with lens turret.

rotation. In the camera of Fig. 2-7, the large knob near the bottom of the panel is the turret knob. The electromechanical method incorporates an electric motor to drive the turret. The electromechanical method offers the advantage of remote-control start and stop of the turret motor. The manual method is the least expensive; the electromechanical is the most expensive. When the camera must be installed in a position that is not readily accessible to an operator and it is necessary that the field of view be changed, the remote-control capability of the electromechanical method is certainly one solution to the problem.

Remote control of the camera primary controls is another popular feature. This feature is desirable when the camera is installed in a location where it is not convenient to position an operator. For example, if CCTV is used for outdoor surveillance of the perimeter of a building or a compound, remote control is practically essential. In such instances, the camera is usually mounted on a high pole or on top of a structure to provide the desired viewing angle. Lighting conditions can change considerably from bright summer sunshine to midnight blinding rain through which floodlights cannot readily penetrate. The ability to adjust brightness and contrast at the camera as well as at the monitor might very well make it possible for the viewer at the monitor to see a useful picture. Fig. 2-8 shows a camera with a remote-control feature. In this unit the back panel which con-

Courtesy Continental Electronics

Fig. 2-7. Turret control knob on rear of camera.

Courtesy Sylvania Electric Products, Inc.

Fig. 2-8. Rear panel of camera removed for remote operation.

tains the focus, brightness, contrast, and turret controls is easily removed. An extension cable is then connected between the removed panel and the camera for remote operation.

Once set, the focus control of the monitor or TV receiver seldom has to be readjusted, because this control focuses the electron beam of the picture tube. This is not related, except by spelling, to optical focus of the lens system of the TV camera. As in 16-mm motion-picture film photography, the camera lens must be refocused as objects come closer to or move farther away from the camera. Optical focus can be accomplished by changing the spacing between the lens and the film in a film camera and between the lens and the vidicon in a TV camera. In a TV camera, either the lens or the vidicon can be moved. For simplicity of design, the lower–cost cameras and those that are designed for stationary installation depend on the movement of the lens.

Closed-circuit television cameras intended for applications where the distances between the subjects and the cameras are continually changing cannot conveniently use this method of optical focusing. There is always the danger that the operator will place his hand over the lens or jar the camera while blindly reaching around from his position behind the camera. Studio-type cameras, therefore, are equipped with optical-focus knobs, handles, or levers. The focus control is usually located at the right side of the camera housing as shown in Fig. 2-9. This knob is mechanically linked to the vidicon assembly. Rotating the control manually moves the vidicon assembly smoothly forward or backward on a track, thereby changing the physical distance between the lens system and the vidicon. Electromechanical techniques are used in some cameras. Motors are actuated to shift the position of the vidicon assembly in relation to the lens. Obviously, an advantage of the electromechanical optical focus control is found in the capability for remote control. The camera in Fig. 2-8 incorporates a remote optical focus control.

It is standard practice among manufacturers to provide a reinforcement at the base of the camera housings. This reinforcement is invariably tapped and threaded to accept conventional 10-24 machine screws. This is done so that the camera can be mounted on a tripod of the type used in photographic work. Dollies, or wheeled bases for tripods, are also available to provide mobility.

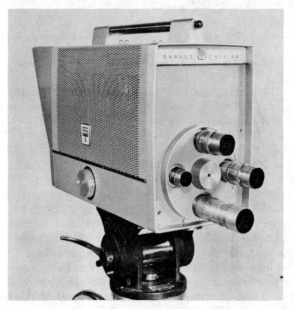

Courtesy Sarkes-Tarzian, Inc.

Fig. 2-9. A camera with the optical focus knob on the right side.

THE CAMERA CHAIN

The phrase "camera chain" is used in reference to the vidicon assembly, its associated electronic chassis and components, and its power supply (Fig. 2-10). There are excellent cameras that combine all assemblies and electronic subassemblies within a

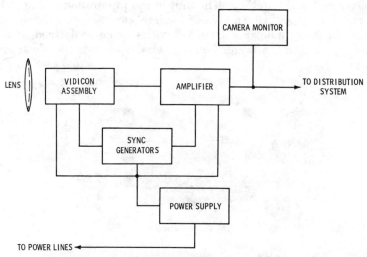

Fig. 2-10. Block diagram of the camera chain.

single housing. Some are surprisingly compact, even though they contain all the circuits necessary for operation. Other cameras, especially those designed for studio use, separate the associated electronic and power-supply chassis from the vidicon assembly. This practice is prevalent among those installations that make use of a central control room overlooking the studio. Whether or not they are separate from each other has little bearing on the ability of the camera to reproduce a scene with high fidelity. Separate facilities are an operational convenience in multicamera setups within the same studio. In such a setup the operator in the control room, because he has the primary and secondary controls for each of the cameras within his own facility, can readily adjust and balance those controls for uniformity of performance from camera to camera.

Industrial applications for closed-circuit cameras may require unusual compactness. For example, it may be necessary to lower a vidicon into a very narrow well-shaft for visual inspection of the interior. It would be impractical to insert the entire camera and its housing into such a shaft. Cameras intended for such applications, therefore, are made available in separated assemblies (Fig. 2-11). The vidicon assembly (Fig. 2-11A) with its lens is enclosed in a watertight tubular housing 2½ inches in diameter. It is connected by cables to its associated electronic and power-supply units (Fig. 2-11B), which remain outside the well-shaft. The operator can adjust the controls for optimum picture while viewing the screen of the monitor. Transistor circuitry is employed to reduce weight and size. The unit in the foreground of Fig. 2-12 is called a "joey." It is a vidicon assembly in its own subhousing. Like the baby kangaroo from which its name is derived, it fits into a pouch in the larger housing which contains the electronic

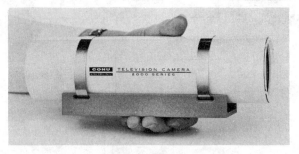

(A) Vidicon assembly.

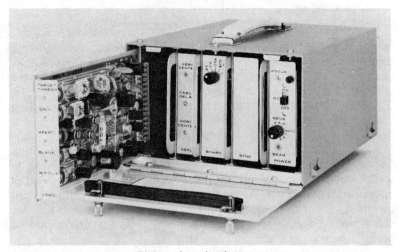

(B) Control panel and circuitry.

Courtesy Cohu/KinTel Electronics

Fig. 2-11. A compact industrial camera.

control circuitry. When exceptional compactness or portability is required, the "joey" is lifted from its pouch and used within the limits of its long extension cable.

TUBES OR TRANSISTORS?

The first closed-circuit TV cameras were designed with electronic tubes. However, as with all electronic equipment, transistors are replacing tubes in certain circuit functions. Today there are all-tube, all-transistor, and hybridized tube-transistor cameras being produced.

Much is already known about the special features of transistors. They are smaller than tubes, and they run cooler. Therefore, it follows that transistorized equipment can probably be made more compact than equipment with tubes. Lower temperatures make it possible to "crowd" parts and transistors into a small cabinet.

Courtesy Sylvania Electric Products, Inc.

Fig. 2-12. The vidicon assembly removed from the front of main housing for portable operation.

Transistors are lighter than tubes and use less power. Because of these facts, it is possible to use batteries or relatively small power supplies with transistorized equipment. Thus, a transistorized closed-circuit television camera is also possibly lighter in weight than is a tube camera.

Tubes, on the other hand, are larger, hotter, and heavier, and demand larger power supplies than transistors. However, they offer electrical characteristics that are not always provided by a transistor substitute. For example, tubes offer higher voltage-amplification and, in many instances, lower inherent noise. In certain sections of television cameras, these last two characteristics become critical with respect to the overall performance of the camera. High amplification affects the sensitivity of the camera to low illumination scenes. Low noise is essential for high-quality picture reproduction.

It is possible to produce transistorized cameras that offer all the performance values of tube-type cameras in closed-circuit television applications. However, the circuits of a high-quality all-transistorized camera are considerably more complex. The complexity is a necessity in order to compensate for such factors as lower amplification and higher noise of the transistors. All-transistor cameras can match the picture performance capabilities of tube-type cameras. In accomplishing the job, however, the all-transistor camera sometimes gets as large physically as the tube-type camera. In any event, the advantage of lower weight is retained; an all-transistor camera will weigh about one-third to one-half less than a comparable tube-type camera. In addition, the transistorized camera is cooler. Often no vent holes are required in the housing of a transistor unit, whereas a tube camera always requires such venting.

Hybridized cameras offer the combination of many of the advantages of transistors with those of tubes. In hybrid units tubes are employed in the critical high-amplification low-noise stages only. In all cases, the vidicon is the same—a tube. Technology has not yet reached the point where the "eye" of the camera can be replaced with a transistor or other semiconductor device. There are reasons to believe that in the future this will be possible. Perhaps then the 6½-inch-long vidicon will be replaced by a device that is only a fraction of an inch in depth. The imagination is free to wonder about the capabilities of so compact an equivalent of the vidicon assembly or "joey." The industrial and scientific applications for such an instrument would be almost unlimited.

The trend toward transistorization of monitors is in process; however, it is very slow. Television cameras are frequently moved from place to place, so obvious benefits are derived from transistorization. At this point, the ability of transistors to withstand severe mechanical shock becomes an important advantage in television cameras. Monitors in closed-circuit television applications, on the other hand, are generally mounted in a fixed location. Therefore, for a given screen size and with today's techniques of assembling the elements of a TV receiver or monitor into a relatively small housing, the compactness of transistorization is of doubtful value. Because the monitor is in a fixed location, weight is of little consequence. The heat generated by the tubes is usually vented conveniently—either by fans (forced-air cooling) or by natural convection and chimney effects of the cabinet.

ELECTRONIC VIEWFINDERS

A film camera is always equipped with an aperture called a *viewfinder*. Looking through his viewfinder, the photographer can see the exact area to which the film will be exposed when he releases the lens shutter. This facilitates composing and balancing the scene to achieve the desired visual effect. In addition, an optical focusing means is frequently coupled to the viewfinder of the film camera. This assures the photographer that the focal point of the composition is in sharp focus. The equipment that enables the television camera operator to accomplish the same optical control is referred to as an *electronic viewfinder*.

Actually, the electronic viewfinder is a small-screen VF monitor. Because of the close viewing distance, a 5-inch screen size is quite popular for the viewfinder and some are equipped with 3-inch screens. Professional cameras may have 8-inch screens. A hood is invariably provided with the camera to keep unwanted outside lighting from striking the viewfinder screen. An example of a closed-circuit television camera with a 5-inch electronic viewfinder screen is shown in Fig. 2-13. Such electronic viewfinders are completely self-contained; that is, they are constructed on a chassis that is separate from the TV camera chassis. They are, however, secured within a common housing or cabinet. The operator adjusts the camera angle and focuses the lenses while looking at the electronic viewfinder.

ACCESSORIES

Almost without exception, manufacturers of closed-circuit TV cameras and monitors supply their units complete and ready for operation after power and interconnecting cables have been applied. However, there are numerous situations where the basic equipment is not completely adequate. Refinements may have to be added to the system to enable it to fit an unusual application or to improve its flexibility.

Camera Lenses

RF and VF cameras using vidicon tubes for picture pickup are usually fitted to accept standard 16-mm motion-picture film-camera lenses. Therefore, such TV cameras are equipped for standard-focusing C-mount lenses with adjustable iris. This gives one a rather extensive choice of lens speeds, fields of view, and quality of optics. Manufacturers who equip their cameras with 2-, 3-, or 4-lens turrets usually supply one lens with the camera. A 25-mm f1.9 all–purpose lens is a popular choice. For operation under low-level lighting conditions, f1.5 lenses are available. Wide-angle and telephoto lenses can be used with closed-circuit TV cameras to achieve effects identical with those achieved with motion-picture film cameras.

Motor-driven focus and iris controls are made available by some manufacturers for use with their own cameras. These afford remote control of the focus and f-stop functions.

Zoom lenses add considerable versatility and flexibility to the operation and utility of any camera. They combine wide-angle through close-up capabilities in a single assembly, eliminating the interruption of the picture that occurs when rotating from one lens to another in a turret-equipped multilens camera. A zoom lens enables continuous variation in field of view while maintaining optical focus. The zoom effect can be controlled manually (Fig. 2-14) or electrically (Fig. 2-15). Both types are available with variable focal lengths as great as 10:1. Generally, lens

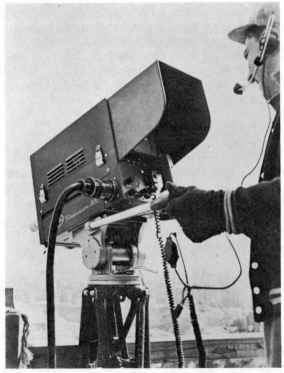

Courtesy General Precision, Inc.

Fig. 2-13. An electronic viewfinder mounted on top of camera.

Courtesy Cannon Camera Co., Inc.

Fig. 2-14. A manually controlled zoom lens.

speeds are slower in zoom lenses, decreasing as focal length is increased. The zoom speed is adjustable on most electrically controlled models. The iris is also adjustable in electrically operated zoom lenses. A remote-controlled zoom lens together with a remote-controlled pan-and-tilt mechanism is considered an exceptionally versatile installation.

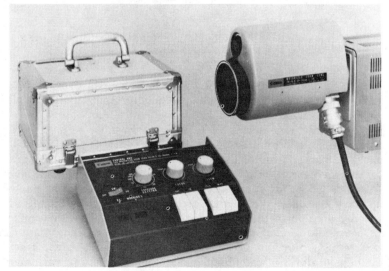

Courtesy Cannon Camera Co., Inc.

Fig. 2-15. An electrically controlled zoom lens and control box.

Pan and Tilt

"Panning" is the action of moving the TV camera in a horizontal plane, right to left, or vice versa. "Tilting" is the action of pointing the camera up or down. Pan and tilt can be performed by adding a "head" to a tripod and mounting the camera on the head. Sometimes a simple ball-and-socket device that enables the camera to be moved or pointed in any direction is used for the head. However, because of the bulk and weight of some cameras, this simple arrangement does not always provide the smoothest control of camera movements. Another type of pan-and-tilt head is shown in Fig. 2-16. The operator grasps the lever which extends

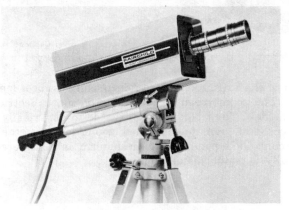

Courtesy Fairchild Camera & Instrument Corp.

Fig. 2-16. A camera mounted on a manually operated pan-and-tilt head.

from the rear of the camera. A locking mechanism is provided to hold the camera in a fixed position. The entire action is manually controlled.

When the closed-circuit television camera must be installed in an inaccessible location or in a hostile environment, an electrically operated pan-and-tilt unit provides the solution to the problem of controlling camera orientation. The control operator uses a lever that is called a "joy stick" (Fig. 2-17). The "stick" can be moved up and down or right and left. Corresponding electrical signals are sent by a cable to the pan-and-tilt mechanism. The TV camera is secured to a small platform on the mechanism. The platform and camera move in accordance with the control signals sent by the operator. By watching the monitor, the operator can orient the camera so that any area within the pan-and-tilt angles of the equipment can be viewed. There is a wide choice available among

Courtesy Pelco Sales, Inc.

Fig. 2-17. Control box for an electrically operated
pan-and-tilt mechanism.

pan-and-tilt mechanisms. The correct choice depends on the weight, bulk, and application for the camera and its mount. There are light, intermittent-duty units, and there are others intended for severe environments, such as underwater or extreme heat or cold. A ruggedized unit intended to withstand severe weather conditions is shown at Fig. 2-18. When connected to the control box and a source of 115-volt 60-cycle AC, the entire assembly rotates on its base for pan action, and the platform tilts for up-and-down movement. The pan is controllable through 350° and tilt through a total arc of 90°. The tilt torque is 90 foot-pounds,

Courtesy Pelco Sales, Inc.

Fig. 2-18. A heavy-duty pan-and-tilt unit.

and the pan torque is 25 foot-pounds. Such high torque is needed to handle the weight added to the TV camera by the environmental housing.

Special Camera Housings

Most closed-circuit television cameras are supplied in housings whose primary function is to protect the operator from any high voltages that may be present in the camera. In addition, they also restrict unwarranted access to the camera interior and provide a simple dust cover. When environmental conditions are abnormally humid, dirty, dusty, hot, or cold, the TV camera must be enclosed in a specially designed housing and constructed of materials capable of surviving such hostile atmospheres.

When a closed-circuit television camera is operated in a volatile, potentially explosive atmosphere, the camera should be enclosed in an explosionproof housing. Such a housing prevents any arc-over within the circuitry from igniting the atmosphere. For example, the use of oxygen and certain anesthetics in the operating rooms of hospitals requires that all precautions be exercised with regard to preventing arcing and sparking in the equipment.

A housing designed to protect the camera from severe climatic conditions is pictured in Fig. 2-19. The camera and lens are in-

Courtesy Pelco Sales, Inc.

Fig. 2-19. An all-weather protective housing.

stalled inside the housing. It can be used with remote-controlled pan-and-tilt as shown. At the front of the housing is a glass window mounted in molded rubber. An extended top cover minimizes moisture runoff into the field of vision of the camera lens. The housing can be equipped with interior insulation to provide temperature protection, filtered air intake, air blower, thermostatically controlled heating element, a windshield washer, wind-

Courtesy Pelco Sales, Inc.

Fig. 2-20. A cylindrical explosionproof camera housing.

shield wiper, thermopane glass window, defroster, and sun shroud. The housing is large enough to accommodate and protect all makes of closed-circuit television cameras. It is feasible to mount a zoom lens on the camera and to mount the housing on a pan-and-tilt mechanism for complete remote control of camera orientation.

Fig. 2-20 illustrates a type of housing used to make an industrial-type closed-circuit television camera resistant to explosion. The front plate assembly is equipped with a thick glass window. Approximately 5 inches of glass area are exposed. When the unit is used with a remote-controlled pan-and-tilt mechanism

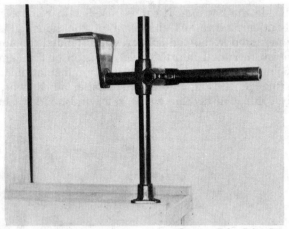

Courtesy Pelco Sales, Inc.

Fig. 2-21. A universal mount for lightweight cameras.

as shown, operators can monitor pictures from the camera while safely positioned behind a barricade or at a long distance from the camera.

Housings are manufactured for use underwater at depths to 250 feet. This type of housing may be constructed of stainless steel, bronze, or aluminum, depending on the requirements of the

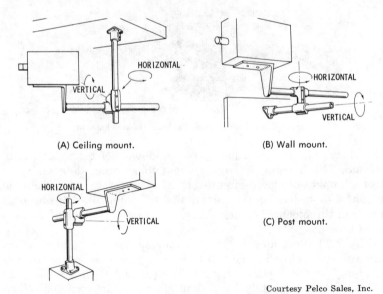

(A) Ceiling mount.   (B) Wall mount.

(C) Post mount.

Courtesy Pelco Sales, Inc.

Fig. 2-22. Various ways in which the mount of Fig. 2-21 can be used.

application. Housings are also available for high-temperature service such as inside or on the periphery of blast furnaces which, without such protection, would destroy the television camera. This type of camera housing is made of stainless steel. It includes a double jacket with a ¾-inch spacing to allow water to be circulated within the jacket for cooling. The front portion of the housing is detachable and can be supplied with water circulating around the circumference of the glass window. Another technique for cooling the window is to use two glass panes with water circulating between them. With pyrex glass, the operating temperature at the glass plate can be as high as 750°F.

Fig. 2-23. A heavy-duty camera mount for shelf or pedestal installation.

Courtesy Davis & Sanford Co., Inc.

Fixed Mounts for Cameras

It is sometimes desirable to install a closed-circuit television camera in a location where it will be inaccessible to unauthorized persons, conserve valuable floor space, or provide the proper viewing angle. When the camera orientation is to be fixed, the system planner can choose from among several types of wall, ceiling, post, or pedestal devices. The one pictured in Fig. 2-21 may be mounted on the ceiling or wall or on a post. Fig. 2-22 shows some typical applications. The L-shaped bracket holds the camera, and the unit is rotatable a full 360° in both the horizontal and vertical planes. Fig. 2-23 shows a heavy-duty unit designed for shelf or pedestal installation. It is fitted with a manual pan-and-tilt head to facilitate installation.

Monitors

I T HAS BEEN POINTED OUT that two types of vidicon cameras are available for consideration in planning a CCTV system—the RF camera and VF camera. Whereas the camera converts a photo image to electrical impulses, the monitor must reconvert those impulses back to a visible image of the original scene. Therefore for optimum operation all monitors within a system must be compatible in performance capabilities with those of the cameras.

DEFINITIONS

In order to understand some of the factors that limit the performance of television systems, you must become familiar with the terminology and its meanings with respect to the picture.

Resolution

The measure of the ability of a system or of a unit of equipment to distinguish fine detail in a scene that is being televised is termed *resolution*. A television picture is composed of a series of lines that run horizontally (with a slight diagonal tilt) across the picture-tube screen in the monitor. The more lines that can be clearly discerned or cleanly separated from each other by the naked eye, the greater are the capabilities of the system to reproduce fine detail. Resolution is expressed in terms of a *number of lines*. As a reference, a typical commercial television set intended for home use and adjusted for optimum performance is capable of resolving approximately 350 lines.

Definition

Popularly called "sharpness," the *definition* of a picture is the product of resolution capabilities plus several other technical factors of performance. There is no number or quantity that can be attached to picture definition. It is entirely a subjective, qualitative value. Definition is determined by the combination of resolution or detail response, gray-scale reproduction capability, signal-to-noise ratio of the overall system, and the criteria of the observer.

Gray Scale

Sometimes confused with "contrast," the gray-scale reproduction capability is simply a high-fidelity retention of the range of light values that intervene between the "black" and the "white" areas of the scene being televised. In all television systems there are inherent limitations with regard to absolute gray-scale fidelity. For example, the screen of a picture tube is not naturally white. In addition, unless it is operated in a completely blacked-out viewing room, the screen is not naturally black. As a further limitation, a television picture tube cannot yield intensities of light to match the maximum intensities of normal scene lighting. If, for instance, a scene contains high-contrast lighting with 1,200 foot-lamberts maximum illumination and 12 foot-lamberts minimum illumination (not unusual), the range of scene contrast is 100 to 1. The dynamic range of a high-quality television monitor is approximately 40 to 1. This limited range compresses the gray scale. In order to take maximum advantage of the capabilities of a closed-circuit television system with regard to gray-scale and contrast ranges, the system planner must become familiar with studio and scene lighting techniques. It is immediately apparent that the range of lighting control should be 40:1 (high lights to shadow areas).

Signal-to-Noise Ratio

"Noise" within a system takes many forms and can be generated in many places. Noise is inherent in the agitated movement of electrons in a wire or component and even the envelope of a vacuum tube. It can be generated by poor electrical contacts and junctions and by electrical motors and switches as they interrupt an electrical current.

In television usage, noise is defined as any spurious, or random, signal entering the television system and having the effect of degrading the quality of the picture. The "signal" part of the term signal-to-noise ratio is the level of the electrical impulses within the system at any fixed point that are exclusively extant for the purpose of reproducing the picture. A high signal-to-noise ratio is, therefore, desired. The higher the ratio is, the better the quality of the picture seen on the television monitor. Signal-to-noise ratios are expressed in terms of decibels (db). The term "db" is used as a reference for the relationship between two known values. It is a figure of merit for performance.

The preceding are the primary factors that determine the quality of the final picture the viewer sees on a television monitor. It is quite proper to use the specific resolution capability of a camera or a monitor as one of the starting points in evaluating the quality of the picture one can anticipate. The monitor should be capable of meeting the specifications (resolution) given for the camera. Of course, the converse is also true.

RF MONITORS

A good-quality television set designed for home use can be used as the monitor for an RF system. As explained in the previous chapter, connection of the coaxial cable from the camera or the line amplifier is made directly to the antenna terminals of the TV set. The TV set is switched to the channel to which the output signal of the RF camera is set. All of the TV set controls are used in exactly the same way they would be if the set were tuned to a commercial-TV station.

Some manufacturers of closed-circuit television equipment have adapted standard television receivers to closed-circuit television service by making simple changes. The set in Fig. 3-1 is essentially a home receiver with several refinements. For example, a three-wire power cord and polarized plug have been added. When it is used for closed-circuit application, the cabinetry is generally simplified, and more durable finishes are applied to the cabinet surfaces. However, any conventional television set can be used with an RF camera. The quality of the picture will, of course, be related to the performance capabilities of the receiver.

In many areas of service, certain special requirements have become generally accepted practice. For example, RF monitors in educational television systems are often specified to be supplied in wooden cabinets. The backs of the monitors are required to be completely enclosed. Three-wire power cables and grounding plugs are specified. Furthermore, all primary controls must be

Courtesy Sylvania Electric Products, Inc.

Fig. 3-1. A typical RF monitor.

placed behind an access panel. Often it is required that the access panel be fitted with a lock. Some of these requirements are specified for reasons of safety, others to prevent or minimize the possibility of tampering with the set. A typical monitor designed for use with RF systems in educational closed-circuit television is shown in Fig. 3-2.

Courtesy Sylvania Electric Products, Inc.

Fig. 3-2. An RF monitor designed for educational applications.

VF MONITORS

RF and VF equipment are not interchangeable without extensive modification of the circuitry. A monitor intended for use with a VF camera will not work with an RF camera, and a VF camera will not work with an RF monitor.

The maximum resolution of an RF monitor is approximately 350 lines. The resolution of a VF monitor, however, can be considerably greater—800 lines is typical of available monitors. VF monitors, sometimes called video monitors, are used extensively in studio work for cuing or previewing the scene picked up by a camera that is to be switched into the system. "Preview" monitors usually employ 8-inch picture tubes. They are installed in the control room of the closed-circuit television facility. The picture that is actually being fed to the system at the moment is monitored on a larger-screen monitor, usually 17- or 21-inch.

VF monitors are available in standard rack size; the panel width is 19 inches, and the height varies according to the screen size. A typical rack-mounting monitor with a 17-inch screen is shown in Fig. 3-3. A space-saving arrangement is feasible when two 8-inch monitors are rack-mounted. As shown in Fig. 3-4, two such monitors can be mounted side by side on a single 19-inch–wide rack panel. Monitors are built into walls, cabinets, and sloping panels of operator consoles. In addition, they are flush mounted on desks or table tops for use as a "prompter," and suspended from ceilings with special mounts designed for that

Courtesy Miratel Electronics, Inc.

Fig. 3-3. A 17-inch screen video monitor designed for mounting in a 19-inch rack.

Courtesy Miratel Electronics, Inc.

Fig. 3-4. Two 8-inch monitors mounted side by side in a 19-inch panel.

purpose. Where a large display is needed, large-screen monitors (up to 27-inch) are used. A typical example of a large-screen monitor is in airline terminals, where plane arrivals and departures are shown as a passenger service. Heavy metal cabinets are used in this type of equipment to assure complete protection. The monitor pictured in Fig. 3-5 has a 24-inch picture tube.

SPECIAL MOUNTS

Large-screen monitors become rather bulky units of equipment. They can become annoying users of valuable floor space when

Courtesy Conrac Div., Giannini Controls Corp.

Fig. 3-5. A 24-inch VF monitor.

they are not in use, unless they are mounted above the floor level. The mount shown in Fig. 3-6 is essentially a U-shaped frame that swivels on a pipe secured to a platform or plate. The monitor is secured at its sides to the *U* frame in such a way as to enable the monitor to be pivoted. The plate can be secured to the ceiling, as in Fig. 3-7, or it can be attached to the wall. With a mount of this type the monitor can be turned and tilted for comfortable viewing from any position.

When it is not convenient to use a ceiling or wall mount, or when it is desirable to be able to move the monitor from one

Courtesy Conrac Div., Giannini Controls Corp.

Fig. 3-6. A monitor mounted in a U-shaped frame that can be tilted and swiveled to any position.

location to another, the mount shown in Fig. 3-8 is preferred. As with the hanging mount, the TV monitor is secured to a *U* frame which provides tilt and rotation capabilities. Large casters are desirable to enable easy mobility. When it is not in use, the entire assembly, mount, and monitor can be rolled into a corner, closet, or store room. Educational institutions frequently use this type of mount. With it, a number of classrooms which require only intermittent use of television can share the equipment. Shelves rigidly secured to a wall are often used. The monitor simply rests on the shelf and is pointed at the audience. Tilting is not a feature of such mounts. With ingenuity, the individual can create a hanger or shelf ideally suited to his needs.

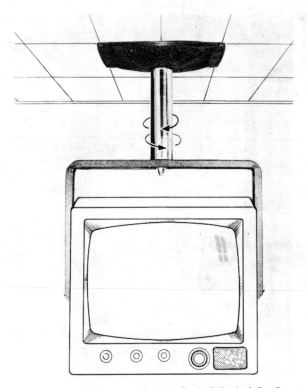

Courtesy Davis & Sanford Co., Inc.

Fig. 3-7. Method of securing monitor mount to ceiling.

SCREEN SIZE

The size of the picture tube in the monitor is determined by the particular application and available space. Another factor in determining size is the distance between the viewer and the set.

Electronic viewfinders vary in screen size from 3 to 8 inches; 5 inches is a popular size. Classrooms or other installations where relatively large groups of people view the picture simultaneously usually require monitors with 23-inch screens. A studio control room might use a 17-inch screen for its personnel. Monitors built into the control-room video-operator console or installations where several monitors are used at the same time to monitor a number of cameras usually have an 8-inch screen. This size is often adequate because of the short viewing distance from the screen. Viewing distances shorter than 3 times the height of the picture tube are considered uncomfortable for long periods of

Fig. 3-8. A floor-type monitor mount
with casters.

Courtesy Davis & Sanford Co., Inc.

time. Five times the height of the picture tube is considered
excellent from the standpoint of comfort and perception of resolution.

PROJECTION TV

Projection TV offers many advantages by providing a larger
screen. For example, in a dental school, when the instructor is
performing with a live patient while lecturing, groups must be
kept quite small so that all can take turns closely observing the
step-by-step procedure. The instructor's progress is considerably
slowed down, and some students are always waiting. A closed-
circuit TV system with the camera focused in a closeup view of
the patient's mouth provides all students with simultaneous participation in addition to a perspective not otherwise possible. In
a conventional CCTV system, the more students, the greater the
number of monitors that must be provided. One could increase
the number of monitors ad infinitum to keep pace with enlarging
groups of students; however, since it is desirable to produce very
large pictures of the instructor's work, projection TV should be
considered.

To give some idea of the capability of projection TV, units can
be obtained that project TV pictures onto a 15 × 20-foot screen

Table 3-1. Size of Screens Covered at Various Distances

Projector Distance from Screen (Ft.)	Screen Height (Ft.)	Screen Width (Ft.)
14	6	8
17	8	10
20	9	12
35	15	20

(Fig. 3-9), large enough for an audience of thousands to view simultaneously. By using several projectors with their screens placed at right angles to each other or back to back, exceptionally large circular or oval-shaped arenas can be covered nicely. Table 3-1 gives the distance between the projector and the screen to achieve screen coverage.

Courtesy Giantview Div., Meilink Steel Safe Co.

Fig. 3-9. A projection-TV system in use in a theater.

Projection-TV Equipment

The projection tube is a picture tube or kinescope capable of extraordinary brilliance. Three screen sizes—3, 5, and 7 inches—are commonly used. The largest size produces the greatest light output. One can expect that the larger the projected picture for a given system, the lower will be both the screen illumination and the resolution. An arrangement of lenses provides the means for focusing the projection tube image onto the screen.

A typical projection system is pictured in Fig. 3-10. The projector tube and optical system are in the unit at the top. The amplifiers, power supplies, and controls are in the wheeled cart below. This particular system can be tuned to Channels 2 through 13. Therefore it can be used with an RF camera as well as for displaying open-circuit telecasts in a closed-circuit system.

Schmidt Optical System

The overwhelming majority of TV projectors use the Schmidt system of optical arrangement. This technique makes use of a parabolic reflector and a corrector lens to project a large amount of light toward the screen. The system is simple, being composed of two optical units with the projection tube located between them as in Fig. 3-11. Reasonable resolution can be expected (on

Courtesy Giantview Div., Meilink Steel Safe Co.

Fig. 3-10. A typical projection-TV system.

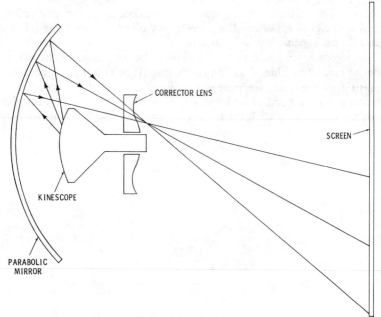

Fig. 3-11. The Schmidt optical system.

the order of 700 lines) when the devices are in optimum alignment. The major advantages of the Schmidt system are simplicity and relative efficiency of forward light transmission.

Front- versus Rear-Screen Projection

Front-screen projection gives the highest-quality pictures with the greatest contrast. However, front-projection screens are quite sensitive to ambient room lighting, which tends to reduce screen brightness. Rear-screen projection gives lower resolution and there is a loss of light in forward transmission through the screen. However, rear-screen projection is less sensitive to the deteriorating effects of ambient room lighting conditions. Contrast is relatively unaffected by wide variations in ambient room lighting.

Ambient Room Lighting

An important consideration in ambient light in the viewing room is, of course, the nature of the activity coincident with the TV projection. If, for example, it is essential that students take notes while viewing, it has been found that 5 footcandles of room lighting are adequate. Care should be taken, when providing room lighting, that lamps are not directed toward the screen.

Lighted blackboards or displays may be used alongside the TV screen, provided their lighting is shielded. In rear projection, ambient lighting behind the screen as well as on the viewing side should be kept as low as possible.

In rear projection it is essential that the area behind the screen be as close to "black" as is practicable. It is common practice to paint the area on the projector side a flat black. When this is impractical, a hood may be made to enclose the projection area within the angles of light transmission (Fig. 3-12). The distance

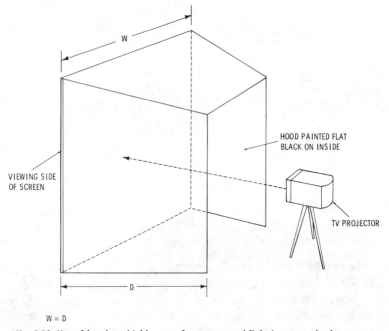

Fig. 3-12. Use of hood to shield screen from unwanted light in rear-projection system.

the hood extends behind the screen should at least be equal to the width of the screen. In other words, distance D in Fig. 3-12 should at least be equal to the width (W). The hood material should be painted a flat black on its inner surfaces to reduce losses through light bounce. It is sometimes adequate to construct a shadow-box or light shield around the screen, depending on the angle of incidence of the unwanted lighting.

Screens

Rigid screens are usually preferred over roll-type screens, where facilities permit keeping the screen in operating position.

In front projection it is often possible to make the screen part of the wall of the viewing room. Sliding panels or drapes may be used to cover it when it is not in use.

Several types of screen material are available. Beaded screens give more brilliance to the pictures than matte screens, but they limit the optimum viewing area (Fig. 3-13). As one moves away from the angle perpendicular to the screen surface, both brilliance

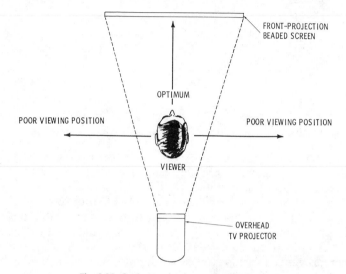

Fig. 3-13. Optimum viewing angle of screen.

and resolution deteriorate. The alignment and size of the elements in a beaded-finish screen have considerable effect on picture quality. Small beads can be expected to provide relatively high picture resolution.

High reflectivity of light is one of the requirements for front-projection screens; however, the viewing surface of a rear-projection screen should have as low a reflection characteristic as possible, without deteriorating the forward light-transmission characteristics. Reduction of reflectivity from the front (viewing) surface of a screen in a rear-projection system makes it possible to increase the ambient room lighting. For this reason, rear screens are made of material polished on one side and matte on the other; they may be used with either side facing the viewers. With the polished side forward, the viewed picture will have greater sharpness and improved contrast. However, the ambient-lighting conditions must determine which side is to be used forward. When the polished surface is used facing the viewers, tilting

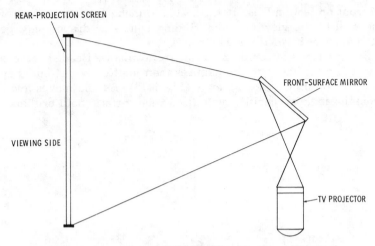

Fig. 3-14. Use of a mirror to increase throw distance in rear-projection systems.

the screen and projector may eliminate disturbing reflections. Otherwise, the matte surface may be used facing the viewers with some sacrifices in contrast and detail.

Often, the area behind or in front of the screen is too limited to allow an adequate "picture-throw" for the desired large-size picture. Fig. 3-14 shows a mirror being used to "bend" the light path from the projector to the screen. A front-surface mirror prevents the appearance of double images on the screen.

Expanding the System

CAMERAS AND MONITORS are the major items in the plan for a closed-circuit television system. A picture can be sent from one location to another with nothing more than these two units of equipment and a length of coaxial cable. However, such a system can be compared with an automobile chassis with body, windows, doors, windshield, windshield wipers, or upholstered seats. The automobile can be operated without these items but the body protects the vehicle and its occupants against weather conditions and makes the chassis usable under varying environmental conditions. The "accessories" multiply the capabilities of the basic equipment and significantly extend the usefulness of the vehicle. This is equally true for television.

A program can be telecast to an infinite number of monitors in a vast audience with just one camera and a few accessories. However, motion-picture film directors learned many years ago that the viewer or audience becomes bored and distracted, and quickly loses interest when a show is produced with a single camera in a fixed position. Viewing a subject at the same angle and at the same distance assures a dull, monotonous telecast. To produce a desirable picture, equipment must be provided that enables panning from side to side, moving in for extreme closeups and out for long shots, changing lenses for variations in the fields of view, varying the visual composition of the scene within the limitations of the 3:4 ratio of the borders of the television frame. In film work the desired effect can be achieved with one camera by laboriously resetting its position and aspect for each new shot. Then the film must be edited, inserting and removing footage, to bring about the desired finished film.

ACCESSORIES IN A ONE-CAMERA INSTALLATION

Efforts are sometimes made in a closed-circuit television system to accomplish dramatic effects using a single camera and zoom lens, tripod, dolly, and manual pan-and-tilt head. All these devices expand the capabilities of a single camera. When the equipment is properly handled, many things can be done with minimal accessories to gain improved assurances of retention of audience interest. However, a severe limitation in this approach is soon realized. The constant motion of the scene as the single camera zooms, pans, and tilts can seriously become a source of disturbance to the viewer. A single, unaccessoried camera may produce boredom, but the overequipped camera can produce an effect on the audience that is best compared with motion sickness.

The moment a second camera is added to the installation, even without accessories beyond a tripod and a dolly, an entirely new concept of telecasting is introduced. This point is illustrated with the type of program frequently used in educational television. The "scene" consists of a lecturer and a chalkboard. Two cameras on wheeled tripods, each with a camera operator, comprise the floor crew. Camera No. 1 is focused in a medium-long view of the lecturer and his chalkboard as the telecast begins. Camera No. 2, not yet feeding the system its picture, is focused in a closeup of the chalkboard. By electrically switching back and forth from camera No. 1 to camera No. 2 at the appropriate moments, the viewers will not become bored by the technical factors in the program. Then, while the chalkboard camera is in use, the second camera can be quickly moved, or a different lens rotated into position to provide a new perspective—perhaps an extreme closeup of the lecturer. When the lecturer turns from the chalkboard, the closeup camera is switched into the system, and the chalkboard camera is removed. The viewers are now concentrating on the lecturer—the chalkboard is out of view. The idle camera is moved quietly back, or a wide-angle lens is rotated into position for an overall view of the lecturer and the blackboard. Thus, with careful thought and planning, it is possible to "choreograph" two cameras to provide an exciting interchange of graphic compositions that are not at all attainable with a single camera in a studio-type operation. The capabilities and versatility of a closed-circuit television system increase in a nonlinear relationship with regard to the increase in physical facilities. Doubling the units of a simple closed-circuit television system achieves considerably more than double its potential as a communications medium.

CONCEPTUAL DIFFERENCES OF SYSTEMS

Educational television (ETV) is a broad label applied to systems used in public schools, colleges, universities, private industrial institutes, and training schools operated by the military. ETV systems usually employ studio techniques wherein two or more cameras are used during the same telecast. Such systems originate programs that are to be fed or transmitted to a number of locations within the school system or district. It is not uncommon in ETV installations to operate several hundred monitors simultaneously, all displaying the same program material.

An industrial television system (ITV) may use as many, or even more, cameras than an ETV system. However, it is quite out of the ordinary for the pictures to be fed to more than a few monitors; frequently only one monitor is in operation at the receiving end of the ITV system. A surveillance situation is a typical example. The security officer is equipped with a single monitor that enables him to selectively survey any one of several areas in which cameras have been installed. The officer operates a switch to select cameras and, if they are part of the installation, "joy sticks" for the remote control of the electric pan-and-tilt heads on which the cameras are mounted.

There are significant conceptual differences between industrial and educational closed-circuit television systems that go beyond the variations in the numbers of monitors in operation. References have just been made to "switching" the cameras. One of the basic differences in equipment concepts between ETV and ITV systems is in the technique for switching cameras, and the location of the switches in the system. Camera switching in educational television systems is performed at the camera location; viewers have no direct control over this function. In an industrial system, the viewer is the operator of the camera switcher.

CAMERA SWITCHERS

The simplest form of camera switcher is a rotary-type selector. An electrical contact in the form of a metal tab secured to an insulating wafer is affixed to a rotatable shaft. The shaft is equipped with a detent action. At each "stop" on the shaft's rotation, the tab mates with a fixed contactor. There are several such fixed contactors, and each is wired to terminate at a coaxial-cable receptacle, or jack. The coaxial cables from each of the cameras intended for switching are connected to these receptacles. These are known as the *inputs*. The rotatable tab of the switch terminates at a similar receptacle and is known as the *output* of the switcher. The coaxial cable that leads to the monitors connects to this output terminal. Thus, with cameras and monitors connected to the switcher, cameras can be selected at will. A rotary switcher capable of selecting any one of four cameras connected to its input is diagramed in Fig. 4-1.

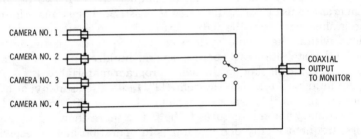

Fig. 4-1. A simple rotary switcher for selecting one of four cameras.

The rotary switcher offers compactness and economy, but it has the disadvantage that you must go through the complete cycle of the rotating action to move from one extreme position to the other. For example, assume that a rotary switcher capable of handling 4 camera inputs is employed. Cameras are usually assigned numbers in sequence. Thus, switch position No. 1 relates to camera No. 1, etc. Should it be desired to switch from camera No. 1 to camera No. 3, one would have to pass through the position for camera No. 2 or No. 4 in order to arrive at No. 3. This is also true in switching from No. 4 to No. 2, and vice versa. This momentary disruption in the continuity of the visual action, and an insertion of an unwanted camera (for an instant), can be quite disturbing to the viewers. In many types of telecasts, such a system is completely unacceptable; however, in industrial television systems, where the picture transmissions are not in the form of "programs," the momentary breaks and intrusions in the continuity of the scenes are of no importance. The rotary-type camera switcher, therefore, finds acceptance in industrial closed-circuit television systems.

As the number of cameras in a system is increased, the use of a rotary switcher becomes more inconvenient and, hence, less desirable. In such cases, push-button switching devices are pre-

Courtesy Radio Corporation of America

Fig. 4-2. A push-button switcher.

ferred. Arranged side by side, the push buttons are mechanically interlocked with each other, making it impossible to have more than one camera feeding the monitor system. Thus, "double exposures" are avoided. With a push-button switcher it is possible to move from camera to camera in any sequence without having to numerically cycle through all camera positions. A typical push-button–type camera switcher is shown in Fig. 4-2. The diagram for this switcher is given in Fig. 4-3.

Switcher-Fader Apparatus

At times during certain types of programs it is desirable to make a less abrupt transition from camera to camera than can be achieved with a switcher. For example, it may be desirable to fade camera 3 out, and fade camera 1 in. In dramatic or theatri-

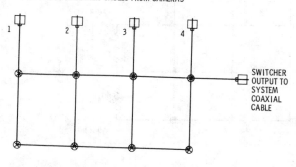

Fig. 4-3. Diagram of push-button switcher with mechanical interlock.

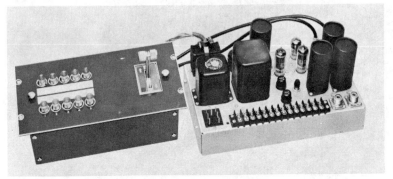

Fig. 4-4. A typical switcher-fader.

cal performances the passage of time is often denoted by the gradual transition from one camera to another. This fulfills the same function as the momentary lowering and raising of the curtain in a theater. It gives performers the moment in time needed to change positions on the set, or to move from one set to another within the studio. It also bridges the change of mood or sustains the mood that has been generated by the action just concluded. The apparatus that enables cameras to be controlled in this manner is known as a *switcher-fader*. In the typical unit shown in Fig. 4-4 the mechanically interlocked push buttons are combined with the dual levers at the right for control of picture intensity. The diagram of the unit (Fig. 4-5) shows that an individual fader

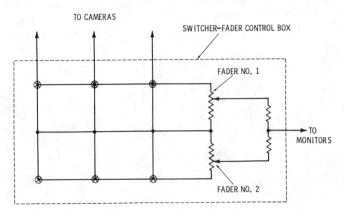

Fig. 4-5. Diagram of a push-button switcher-fader.

control is used for each row of push buttons. The fader control for a television camera may be compared with the volume control of a phonograph; both control the strength of signals, the latter controlling sound and the former controlling picture. The volume control of the phonograph operates in a rotary manner; camera-fader controls move in a straight line. Instead of knobs, as with volume controls, camera fader controls have levers secured to the shafts of the components that cause the fade action. The component is so installed that the lever must be moved vertically to actuate the control. There are several reasons for this: A number of controls can be mounted side by side, making it possible to operate a number of faders with one hand; vertical motion is more natural from a seated position; and the physical panel-space requirements are reduced.

The switcher-fader can be operated with one hand, leaving the other completely free to control sound channels or volume controls. It should be brought out at this point that many professional sound-mixing consoles (where a large number of microphones must be operated simultaneously, requiring continuous balancing and fading) use the vertical linear-acting controls for sound. This same concept of control is used in multiengine aircraft where side-by-side vertical-action levers simultaneously control the engine speeds.

The fade control is electrically located between the push-button switches and the system that distributes the picture to the monitors. By manual control, you can slide the fade lever downward, diminishing the signals from the camera connected to the depressed push button. At the extreme downward position of the fader the picture becomes completely extinguished. During the moment the monitor screens go dark, the push button for the next camera is depressed. This action removes the connection between the first camera and the fader and replaces it with a connection between the second camera and the fader. As the fade lever is moved upward, the picture from the second camera becomes visible on the monitor screens, reaching maximum brilliance when the fade lever is at its extreme upper limit. With a little practice, fast or slow fades and transitions from camera to camera can be quite skillfully accomplished.

The two fader controls in Figs. 4-4 and 4-5 make it possible to cross-fade, dissolve, and overlap, or superimpose pictures from two separate cameras. As an example of the dramatic effects that can be accomplished with such a provision, consider the telecasting of a performance by a music soloist such as a violinist. One camera can be set up for a long shot, showing the artist in a full-length view; a second camera set up for an extreme closeup of a fingering of the violin strings. The dual faders can be adjusted at an intermediate point in their vertical travel limits, and, with both cameras "punched up" on the push buttons, the viewers gain an interesting composite picture. Either of the two cameras can be faded in or out at will, or both can be faded together. The two horizontal rows of push buttons connect any of the cameras in the system to either of the two fader controls. The faders work in reverse order with respect to each other. In the extreme upward position, one control fades in while the other fades out. Their effects are reversed at the downward positions of the faders; the first one fades out and the second one fades in. If one were to depress the camera-1 push button in the top row, a mechanical interlock would make it impossible to depress the same push button in the lower row. However, the camera-2 push button in the lower row, for example, can be depressed without disturbing the camera-1 push button in the top row. Thus, cross fades from one camera to the other are obtained by simply holding both levers of the fader controls with one hand. As has been pointed out, at an intermediate position the pictures from both cameras become simultaneously visible.

DISTRIBUTION AMPLIFIERS

The strength of the output signal from any closed-circuit television camera imposes certain limitations. The camera cannot be expected to supply pictures for an infinitely large number of television monitors or an unlimited footage of coaxial cable. While there is no practical limit to the size of a closed-circuit television system, at some point in the growth of an installation it becomes necessary to reinforce the strength of the signals provided by the camera. The unit of equipment that achieves this reinforcement is known as a *distribution amplifier*, sometimes called a *line amplifier*. The function of this unit can be compared to booster amplifiers used in public-address sound systems for large areas. To return to our previous analogy, start with a conventional record player, or phonograph, that is adequate for home use. It cannot be expected to provide a sound loud enough to fill even a small area. There are residual noises in the area that must be competed with. Crowds contribute noise that must be overridden by the sound from the record player. In addition, there are natural losses in the transmission and dispersion of sound through the atmosphere separating the record player from the far end of the area.

The losses or inadequacies of the native capabilities of the original record player demand the addition of a booster amplifier to sig-

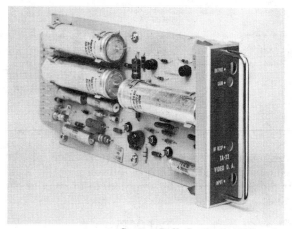

Courtesy Radio Corporation of America

Fig. 4-6. A transistor plug-in distribution amplifier.

nificantly step up the strength of the signal from the record player. It is the same with television cameras; there are losses caused by electrical leakage in the dielectric material of the interconnecting coaxial cables, losses due to electrical resistance of the coaxial cable conductors, and noise and interference within the system as well as from outside that must be overcome. In a closed-circuit television system the distribution amplifier acts as the booster of the signals from the television camera. It assures that the losses, noises, and interference will not depreciate the clarity and sharpness of the pictures viewed on the monitors. An unusually compact transistor distribution amplifier is shown at Fig. 4-6. This unit is designed for plug-in connections.

It has been mentioned that coaxial cables introduce losses in signal strength to any system. If one were able to measure the strength of the signal voltage from the camera at intermittent points along the cable in a simple system consisting of a camera, a monitor, and a coaxial cable, the voltage would decrease as the distance from the camera is increased. At some point along the cable the difference between the voltage inserted by the camera into the cable and the voltage of the inherent noise within the cable becomes too small for proper monitor operation. In an earlier chapter it was brought out that the ratio of the difference between signal and noise was a factor in determining picture sharpness; the higher the signal-to-noise ratio, the better the visible results are. A distribution amplifier inserted between the camera and the coaxial cable, or at other points in the system where losses become pronounced, helps maintain the signal-to-

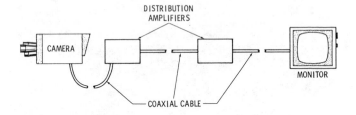

Fig. 4-7. Distribution amplifiers connected in a long coaxial cable.

noise ratio essential to optimum performance of the system. Fig. 4-7 shows the location of distribution amplifiers in a simple system using an exceptionally long length of coaxial cable.

TAPOFFS

If monitor after monitor is connected to a common cable, inter-action between the monitors will result. Adjustments to one monitor will affect the performance of others. In addition, the individual monitors will perform poorly, behaving as though the signals to their inputs were weak. One popular technique used to prevent these troubles is to employ a device called a *tapoff*. Its popularity is due to its simplicity. A tapoff (Fig. 4-8) is installed at the point along the cable that is physically near to the monitor location. Electrically, the device has three terminations: (1) input from the camera end of the system, (2) output to the monitor, and (3) output to the balance of the system.

EQUALIZERS

Despite the advantages of coaxial cables in carrying the signals from camera to monitor over long distances, their disadvantages must be considered. The electrical losses that cause attenuation of the overall signal strength have already been considered. How-

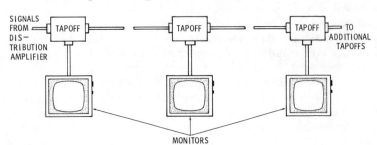

Fig. 4-8. The use of "tapoffs" to isolate monitors.

ever, the characteristics of the attenuation must be further examined. The addition of a booster or distribution amplifier alone is not always adequate assurance of optimum system performance.

The signals from the closed-circuit television camera cover a broad spectrum of frequencies, considerably broader than the spectrum of the highest high-fidelity audio amplifier ever made. In audio amplifiers there are tone controls for treble and bass sounds. By adjusting these tone controls, you can enable the equipment, in conjunction with the accessories, to have a "flat frequency response." This form of response brings the reproduced sound from the speaker as close as possible to that of the original performance. In effect, the tone controls are compensating for electrical losses that may have been introduced by a component, or even by a length of cable, within the overall system. Usually, such losses are the greatest at one or more portions of the frequency spectrum. The tone controls "equalize" the frequency-selective losses. This is analogous to the character of the losses introduced to a closed-circuit television system by the coaxial cable. The signal voltages that are essential to high-fidelity reproduction of the television picture are not evenly attenuated over the entire frequency spectrum used by the video amplifiers in the camera and the monitor. The attenuation, due to losses in the dielectric material, as well as in the conductor of the coaxial cable, is pronounced at the high-frequency end of the video spectrum. The effect at the monitor is an inability to reproduce pictures that are as sharp as those that can be attained. Another phenomenon known as *phase shift* also occurs. Phase shift causes smearing of the picture and, of course, contributes to a depreciation of the picture quality. When coaxial cables in excess of 1,000-foot lengths are used, such selective attenuation of the spectrum and phase distortion can be anticipated. As with the audio amplifier, a special equalizer becomes necessary when attenuation and distortion become visibly significant. The equalizer circuitry exhibits electrical characteristics that complement the losses, resulting in a reasonably flat frequency response throughout the usable spectrum. The equalizer also contains components and circuitry to correct the phase distortion.

Usually the equalizer is installed at the input, or ahead of the distribution amplifiers as shown in Fig. 4-9. This helps prevent overloading or "swamping" the equalizer, which would reduce its effectiveness. Equalizers are passive devices; that is, they do not provide amplification of the signal. In fact, by the very nature of the way they do their jobs they introduce losses of their own. These losses are referred to as the *insertion loss*. The quantity of the loss is expressed in decibels (db). The magnitude of the loss is usually in the order of 6 db, or 50% of the signal voltage for each 1,000-foot of coaxial cable. Amplifiers must be included in the system to compensate for this insertion loss. If the coaxial cables shown in Fig. 4-9 are of significantly different lengths, it may be necessary to provide an individual equalizer ahead of each distribution amplifier.

There are also combination equalizer-amplifiers. The output level of such units is usually the same as its input level, resulting in an overall amplification factor of 1, or unity. Thus, the overall effect is neither that of loss nor gain; it is purely that of equalization.

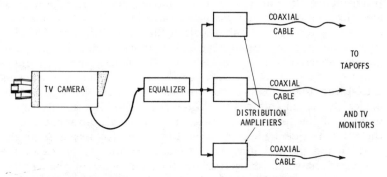

Fig. 4-9. Equalizer connected in circuit to compensate for cable losses and phase shift.

ISOLATION AMPLIFIERS

Video monitors are essential to control-room operations. Obviously they provide a means to see exactly what is going out to the system, or what is to be sent out with the next operation of the camera switcher. The latter is known as *previewing*, or *cuing*. If the control-room monitor were switched from line to line (from camera signal to camera signal) without some technique for electrically isolating the effects of the monitor as a load, an instantaneous impulse might be fed to the entire system each time the monitor is switched. *Isolation amplifiers* provide such separation and preclude the transient effects of monitor switching.

SYNC GENERATORS AND POWER SUPPLIES

One of the requirements for the operation of any television system, whether closed or open circuit, is that equipment for synchronizing certain circuits in both the camera and the monitor must be included. For example, the circuit that controls the motion of the electron beam in the picture tube of the monitor (moving it across the screen in a diagonal) must be synchronized with a circuit in the camera that controls an electron beam directed at the photosensitive face of the vidicon tube. The two electron beams must start from top to bottom on their respective tube faces at the same instant. When the electron beams of all vidicons and picture tubes within a system are in step with each other, they are synchronized, or "in sync." When they are not in sync, the picture appears to roll, or one sees a multiple number of wide diagonal lines across the screen. The unit of equipment that supplies the timing signals to the system is called a *sync generator*. The impulses are neither visible nor audible in a properly adjusted system. It is common practice to incorporate sync generators within the design of individual monitors. The sync generator for a closed-circuit television camera may be small enough to be included within the camera housing. In a simple closed-circuit television system, self-contained cameras are usually employed. However, in complex systems where many cameras and monitors are used, the sync generator is often unitized. It is mounted on a chassis of its own and installed within the main equipment or control room. The synchronizing signals are then fed simultaneously to all cameras from that master generator. This practice assures that all cameras will be in step with each other. It is also highly desirable, but not always possible, to use the same sync generator to time the circuits of the monitors in the system.

Of course the electronic equipment, cameras, monitors, isolation, distribution, and equalizer amplifiers must be provided with their operating voltages at specified currents. There is no rule as to where the power supplies should be located and there are many variations in practice. Some cameras contain their own power supplies within their housings, and some do not. However, almost all monitors contain their own power supplies. The power supplies for amplifiers are almost always located on separate chassis. When power supplies are separate from their associated equipment, they are usually installed in the control room associated with the studio in which the cameras are located. The power supply can be mounted inside the operator console or, as is more often the custom, in a standard 19-inch-wide enclosed metal rack (Fig. 4-10). All connections for the cameras are terminated at multicontact wall jacks inside the studio. A mating plug and a multiconductor flexible cable connect the camera to the jack and thus to the control room equipment. Power supplies may dissipate considerable heat, so provisions must be included in the system plan for air conditioning. This may not be more than a ducted fan or air blower installed to provide a stream of air to keep the ambient temperatures down.

Racks of equipment may be installed side by side in a control room, as shown in Fig. 4-11. These racks contain the control circuits associated with the systems operation. The primary controls for the camera are located on an operator console (not visible).

Courtesy Radio Corporation of America

Fig. 4-10. Power supplies, sync generator, and control circuitry mounted in 19-inch metal rack.

TALLY LIGHTS

The tally light is a desirable feature for cameras intended for studio operations in a closed-circuit television system. Virtually any type of lamp with a small aperture can be used as a tally light; it is actuated simultaneously by the camera switcher to indicate which camera in a multicamera setup is in use at the moment. Thus, performers know in which direction to "look" during the telecast. In addition, floor personnel and cameramen

Courtesy University of Akron

Fig. 4-11. Racks of equipment installed side by side in a control room.

are always aware of the "condition" of their cameras with respect to the flow of the telecast. It is desirable to have the tally light mounted so that it is visible from any eye level position within the studio. Some cameras have the tally lights on top of the camera; others at the front and rear panels; still others install them at top, front, and rear. Fig. 4-12 shows an excellent arrangement for tally lights that provides high all-around visibility.

MOTION PICTURE FILM AND SLIDE PROJECTION

Programming for television often makes excellent use of motion-picture film, transparencies, and opaque graphic arts materials. Excellent reproduction of all such media is achieved with 16- or 35-mm film, or slides—black and white or color, positive or negative. Of course, the quality of the picture at the monitor is dependent on the quality of the units of equipment used in projecting the films and slides.

It is entirely possible to achieve a degree of usable quality with motion-picture projectors such as those used in the home and classroom; however, there are limitations inherent in such equipment when they are applied to television service. These limitations must be taken into account if such equipment is to become a fixed accessory to the closed-circuit system. Conditions considered tolerable when viewed directly from a projector screen cannot be tolerated on the screen of a picture tube. This is no doubt due to several causes. For example, when switching from a "live" performer on camera to a filmed performer, any degradation of the picture will be quite apparent to the viewer. Usually this becomes objectionable and disturbs the viewer.

Among the limitations inherent in home or classroom motion-picture film projectors are the inability to start and stop instantly without appreciable lag or coasting. The inability of these projectors to operate continuously without significant variations in speed and to have no apparent vertical jitter or lateral weaving motions is especially disturbing. The standard scan rate for television systems in the United States is 30 frames per second. Motion-picture film has a standard scan rate of 24 frames per second. Film projectors for television, therefore, are either designed or specially adapted to be synchronous with television without altering the apparent speed of the projected film. Their film drive mechanisms are made synchronous with the AC power

Courtesy Radio Corporation of America

Fig. 4-12. Tally lights mounted on front and rear of camera.

Courtesy Radio Corporation of America

Fig. 4-13. A 16-mm motion-picture projector for television use.

line frequency that operates both the projector and camera systems. Film projectors for television installation are more durably constructed than those intended for classroom or home viewing. The optical systems of television projectors, whether motion-picture or slide type, are considerably superior. Film threading is usually simplified, and bulb-changing mechanics are designed to enable rapid replacement if a failure should occur while the projector is in operation. A typical 16-mm motion-picture film projector intended specifically for television service is shown in Fig. 4-13. A professional-quality 35-mm motion-picture film projector for television service is shown in Fig. 4-14. Fig. 4-15 shows the optics of a television projector for 16-mm motion-picture film.

Multiplexer

Motion-picture film and slides must be projected onto the face of a vidicon tube of a television camera for distribution to the

Fig. 4-14. A 35-mm motion-picture film projector for television service.

Courtesy Radio Corporation of America

closed-circuit television system. Often a single camera is used for a group of projectors, rather than a separate camera for each projector. An optical system known as a *multiplexer* provides the method for this. As shown in Fig. 4-16, mirrors are positioned so that the image can be directed from the projector to the vidicon. The mirror system is made movable by mounting the mirrors on bases which are rotated either manually or by motors or solenoids. Moving the mirrors bends the light path from the projector in use to the vidicon. A photograph of the unit diagrammed in Fig. 4-16 is given in Fig. 4-17. Dichroic mirrors are also used in some systems. They are positioned so that as a projector is started, its light beam is directed at the vidicon without requiring further adjustment, rotation, or movement of the mirror system.

The multiplexer in Fig. 4-18 is designed to provide a multiple picture input system of optics for a single vidicon camera. This particular unit can accommodate two 16- or 35-mm motion-picture film projectors and one slide projector. An accessory makes it possible to use a fourth projector. This fourth projector could be of the type used with opaque illustrations or another slide projector. As shown in Fig. 4-19, the multiplexer uses two beam-splitting cubes (prisms) for transmitting and reflecting images from the projectors directly onto the target face of the vidicon through a field lens. This system permits a permanent arrangement of the film apparatus. Either of the motion picture or slide

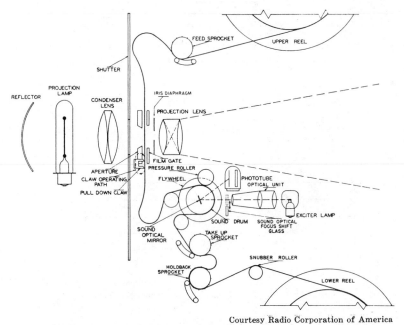

Courtesy Radio Corporation of America

Fig. 4-15. The optical system in a typical 16-mm motion-picture projector for television service.

projectors may be switched on or off electrically while the optical system remains stationary. The accessory for the fourth projector (shown in dotted lines) includes a moving mirror and a field lens which is inserted for use in the optical path by the use of manual or remote electrical controls. The equipment is mounted on a rigid pedestal for mechanical stability. Two adjustable shelves are provided for leveling the vidicon camera and the slide projector. The field lens and the prisms are mounted on adjustable optical bench plates to provide a means for leveling the optics. A cover fits over the multiplexer to make it light–tight and dust–free. Remote control operation of the multiplexer and projector is feasible and desirable in the closed-circuit television plan. The controls

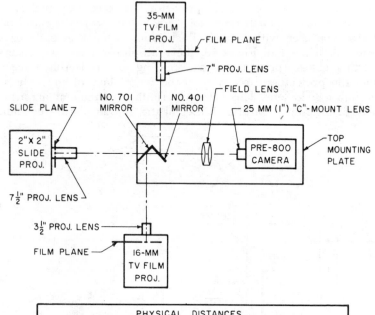

PHYSICAL DISTANCES		
16 MM	FILM PLANE THRU MIRRORS TO ₵ OF FIELD LENS =	47"
35 MM	" " " MIRROR " " " " " =	53"
2" X 2"	MIRRORS =	42"

CENTER OF FIELD LENS TO THE FILM PLANE IN ALL CASES

Courtesy General Precision, Inc.

Fig. 4-16. The optical system of a typical multiplexer.

are usually installed at the master console operator's position, or at the director's table in the same control room. After having mounted and threaded all film, the control-room operator simply pushes a button to start the projector; another button operates the camera switcher, or the switcher-fader feeds the output of the vidicon camera on the multiplexer to the entire system.

3-D CLOSED-CIRCUIT TELEVISION

Conventional TV cameras and monitors transmit and display 2-dimensional pictures; they are incapable of producing the dimension of depth. In certain industrial processes and scientific research areas the depth dimension (3-dimensional aspect) cannot be eliminated without serious loss of control of the process or work at hand. In processes which are hazardous to human

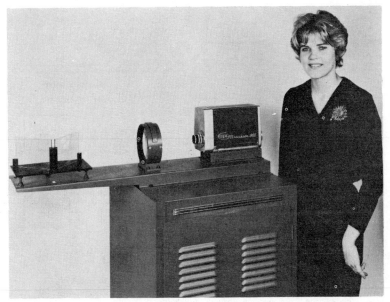

Courtesy General Precision, Inc.

Fig. 4-17. Photo of the multiplexer diagrammed in Fig. 4-16.

Courtesy Radio Corporation of America

Fig. 4-18. A multiplexer with provisions for up to four different projectors.

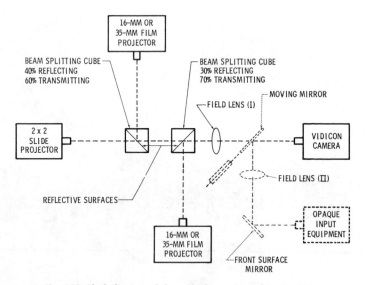

Fig. 4-19. Block diagram of the multiplexer pictured in Fig. 4-18.

beings, closed-circuit television benefits become especially significant. Many techniques for closed-circuit 3-D television have been developed on special order. However, at least one commercially manufactured accessory is available for adapting, rather than converting, standard vidicon cameras and monitors to 3-D use. This accessory (Fig. 4-20) fits onto the lens of the vidicon camera with a simple adaptor ring. Image-splitting is accomplished through the mirror arrangement diagrammed at Fig. 4-21. A precut screen that fits directly over the face of the picture tube on the monitor is supplied. A hood (Fig. 4-22) then fits directly over the face of the screen and the picture tube. The hood contains optics that complement the mirror system of the adapter at the camera and

Fig. 4-20. Adapter to fit over lens of camera for 3-D television.

Courtesy Stereotronics Corporation

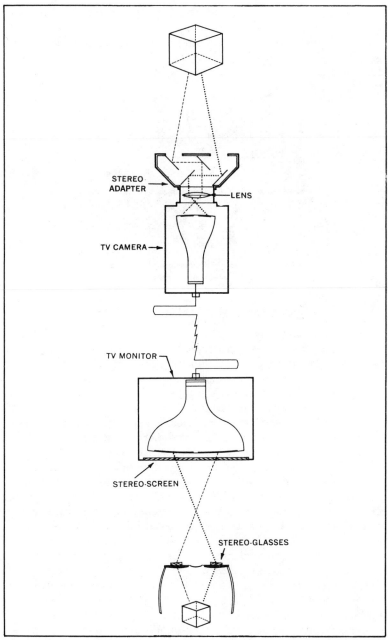

Fig. 4-21. Optical system for the 3-D television system.

reconverge the image that was split at the camera. While this arrangement provides 3-D viewing for the individuals in specialized work functions, it is not suitable for group viewing. Glasses with complementary optics may be worn for group viewing in place of the hood.

Courtesy Stereotronics Corporation

Fig. 4-22. Hood for fitting over picture tube of monitor in 3-D television system.

VOICE INTERCOMMUNICATIONS

In a studio-type operation a means must be provided for conversation between floor-crew members and control-room personnel. Jacks are built into the housings of many TV cameras, and an extra pair of wires included in the multiconductor cables that connect them to the control equipment. Usually a lightweight headset consisting of an earphone and microphone combination similar to those used by switchboard operators in a telephone exchange is provided for the camera operator. Plugs are provided at the ends of the wires of the headset to mate with the jacks in the camera housing. Thus, by interconnection all operating personnel are in contact with managers and the director during the telecast. Following the spoken directions from the control room, the cameramen and other operations personnel in the studio can be instructed to position a camera, get ready for a shot, pan, tilt, or zoom in or out of the scene. The technical action can be paced and, in case of technical difficulty on the floor, the control room can be alerted immediately through the intercom. In addition to the intercom headset, a second earphone enhances the utility of the intercom channel quite dramatically. This second earphone receives the sound signal exactly as it is fed to the closed-circuit system. This enables all studio personnel to hear as well as see the telecast. It also adds to the completeness of the participation of the staff in behalf of the program effort and enables the studio personnel, especially the cameramen, to more closely follow voice cues to which they have been alerted.

AUDIO FOR THE SYSTEM

Up to this point we have been concerned with the pickup and reproduction of the picture exclusively—audio (sound) has been ignored. The reason is that the video aspects are common to all users of television systems, but many closed-circuit systems do not use sound at all. For example, numerous industrial, scientific, commercial, and military installations have no need for sound facilities. However, there are a considerable number of applications in which sound transmission and reception are mandatory.

Two basic techniques for providing sound to the monitor locations are in common use. They are the subcarrier-FM and the direct-line systems. The subcarrier-FM system is usually employed in a system wherein RF-type monitors are used. Such monitors, as has been previously explained, are usually conventional television receivers which have their own self-contained sound amplifiers and speakers.

The direct-line system is the popular choice in a system using video-type TV cameras and monitors. Video monitors do not have self-contained sound channels; therefore, the sound must be provided by cables, audio amplifiers, and speakers that are not an integral part of the monitor circuitry. Both techniques, properly adjusted and operated, are capable of providing excellent high-fidelity sound reproduction.

Subcarrier FM

In the transmission of commercial-TV broadcasts, video and audio signals are separately generated. Both are connected to a common antenna at the transmitter site. The combined signals are received by the TV receiver, separated by internal circuitry, and faithfully reproduced within the receiver. The subcarrier-FM technique of commercial-TV broadcasting can be applied to closed-circuit systems using RF cameras and monitors by adding a sound modulator to the system. The sound modulator is installed in the coaxial cable at a point near to the RF camera. It is connected between the camera and the coaxial cable feeding the system as shown in the diagram of Fig. 4-23. The audio signals from the sound pickup devices (microphone, record player, tape recorder, or film projector) are connected to the sound modulator. The output of the sound modulator contains the electrical signals from the camera, and the signals from the sound devices. The picture and audio signals are fed through the coaxial cable without

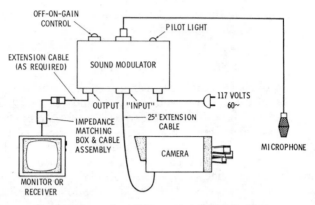

Fig. 4-23. Connection of the sound modulator in system.

modification to the antenna terminals of the TV monitors. In this type of audio system it is important that all TV receivers and sound modulators be properly aligned; they must be electrically stable and not require retuning as they warm up. It is important that the audio signal to the sound modulator be so controlled that it does not cause spurious interference with the picture signal. Such interference manifests itself as a herringbone pattern superimposed on the picture, varying in texture with the audio signal.

Direct-Line Audio

A direct-line audio system uses no frequency converters or subcarrier-FM apparatus, or any connection to the coaxial cable that links the cameras to the monitors. As was mentioned previously, however, it is necessary to provide amplifiers and speakers at the monitor sites. The speakers should be installed as close as possible to the picture tubes of the monitors because a physical separation of sight and sound is very disturbing to the viewer. A typical direct-line audio system intended for use with a single sound source such as a microphone is given in Fig. 4-24. The utility of

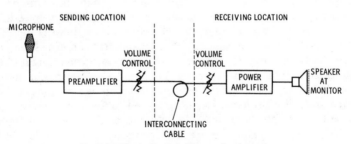

Fig. 4-24. The basic direct-line audio channel.

such an arrangement is of course extremely limited. The system can be improved by the simple addition of an audio switcher (Fig. 4-25) that serves a purpose similar to that served by a camera switcher. The limitations of both switchers are quite similar, until faders are added.

In any direct-line audio plan, a professional mixing console becomes indispensable when more than one sound is used. An audio console (Fig. 4-26) provides controls for switching, fading, mixing or superimposing, and balancing a multiple number of sound-pickup devices. In the system diagramed in Fig. 4-26, the PGRM (program) line feeds the audio power amplifiers at the monitors, and the PA (public address) line connects to an amplifier in the control room for local monitoring.

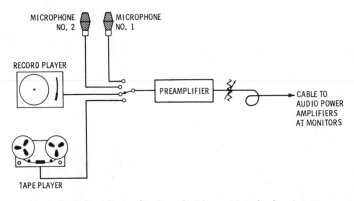

Fig. 4-25. A direct-line audio channel with provisions for four inputs.

A typical console suitable to closed-circuit television applications is pictured in Fig. 4-27, and a diagram of the unit is given in Fig. 4-28. The console contains the volume controls and amplifiers essential to feeding sound signals of proper intensity to the system. A volume (level) indicator (a meter calibrated in decibels) is always part of a well-designed console. It is mounted so that it will be clearly visible without parallax to the console operator. The console or an associated rack cabinet should be equipped with a *patch board*. A patch board is a series of jacks at which cables from the sound sources, cables to the console inputs, and cables to the system are terminated. These jacks enable access to all elements of the sound system and provide extraordinary flexibility to the operations. By "patching in," you can either feed or receive audio to or from the monitor locations; in emergencies (such as a partial breakdown of the equipment), the patch board enables a rapid transfer of circuits. Patch boards are inexpensive

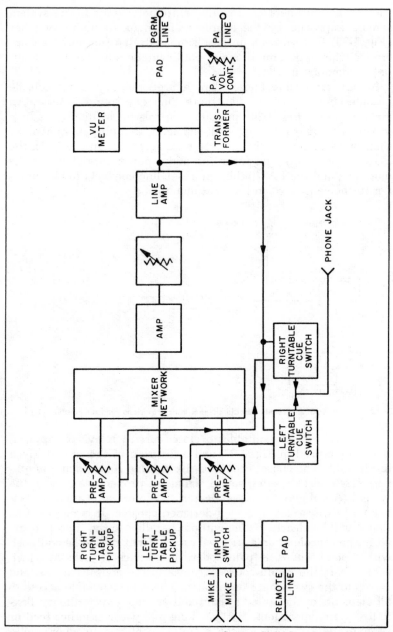

Fig. 4-26. Block diagram of an audio facility that permits mixing, blending, or fading sounds from several sources.

and exceptionally useful; they should be seriously considered in the plan for any closed-circuit system.

AUDIO CUES

In the control room equipped with record- and tape-player mechanisms it is essential that a record or a tape recording be checked to locate a specific sound. This operation is referred to as cuing. (Of course, the sounds of cuing—the running of a tape or record back and forth until the operator is satisfied—must not be allowed to enter the audio channel of the system.) A cue switch and a separate cue amplifier (Fig. 4-29) provide this facility. The

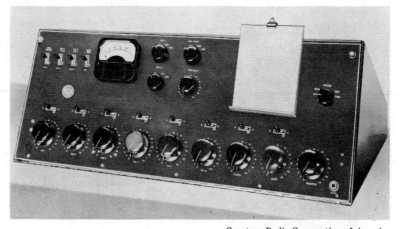

Courtesy Radio Corporation of America

Fig. 4-27. A typical audio console for closed-circuit TV systems.

speaker is located close to the operator in the control room. The switch transfers the input of the cue amplifier to the outputs of the individual sound pickup devices. The cue amplifier is to the audio system exactly what the isolation amplifier is to the video system. Therefore, cue amplifiers are designed so that they do not cause transient impulses to appear in the sound channel as the cue switch is actuated; they must not produce any apparent effect on the sound channel when they are used. The block diagram of a transistor cue amplifier is given in Fig. 4-30. The bridging input components provide electrical isolation between the amplifier and the circuit to which it is connected.

It is sometimes desirable to feed a "cue" from a remote sound source to the studio for the benefit of the floor personnel. If a patch board is included in the control-room equipment, the output

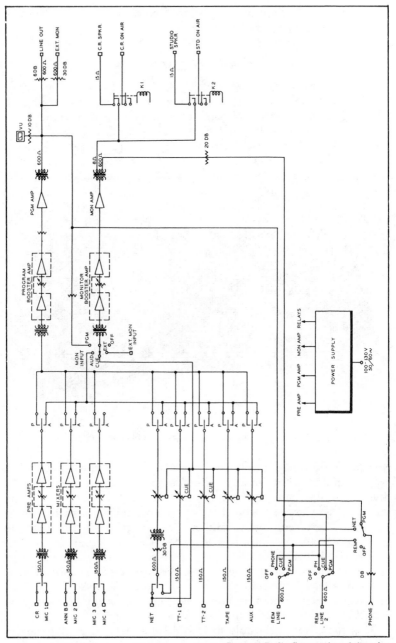

Courtesy Radio Corporation of America

Fig. 4-28. Diagram of the audio console pictured in Fig. 4-27.

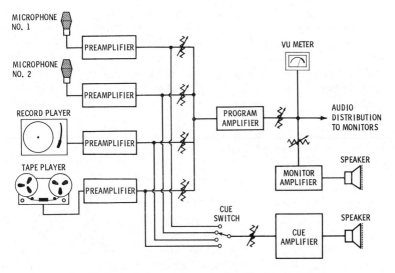

Fig. 4-29. Method of connecting a cue amplifier into the circuit.

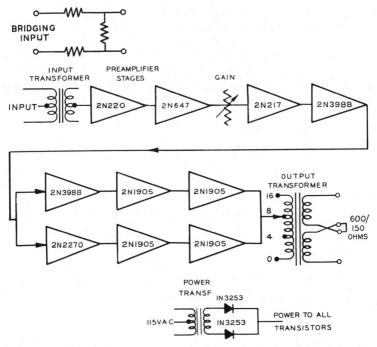

Courtesy Radio Corporation of America

Fig. 4-30. Diagram of a typical cue amplifier.

of the cue amplifier can be connected to the intercom cable through suitable transformers or other isolating components to provide this convenience. Should it be desirable to feed the sound into a speaker inside the studio, an arrangement must be included that automatically disconnects the studio speaker the instant a microphone in the studio becomes active or the output of the audio console is fed to the system. It is customary and advisable to install jacks and earphones inside the studio connected to the output of the cue amplifier. Thus, anyone inside the studio can hear a cue regardless of the action within the studio. In dramatic or musical productions that make use of recorded sounds, this becomes especially useful for last-minute rehearsals of time cues.

Talk-Back System

During rehearsals the director must have some means of talking back to the performers; holding two-way conversations with all participants is a must for directors. The cue amplifier or a separate amplifier may be used for this purpose. A push-button or lever switch is provided at the director's position in the control room. Depressing the button or the switch connects his microphone to the input of the talk-back amplifier, connected to the studio speaker. As with the cuing system, it is important that the talk-back speaker in the studio be disabled when the studio is "live," or on the air. It is feasible to use the same circuits and amplifier for talk back and the voice intercom; however, the details can only be resolved after a complete understanding of the requirements for an individual system are thoroughly analyzed.

Video Recording Techniques

IN MANY CLOSED-CIRCUIT television applications it is not practical to watch the performance "live." Also, it is often desirable to show the same production more than once. This is especially true in educational applications. Therefore, in many installations some means of recording the program material must be provided. Two methods of recording—motion-picture film and video tape—are utilized. Each of these systems will be discussed in this chapter.

KINESCOPE RECORDINGS

Film-recording techniques were well established when television broadcasting and reception became commercially feasible. Motion-picture cameras and projectors were available everywhere. Many people had gained personal experience in "shooting" home movies for parlor projection. Most schools had classroom projectors to show experiments in life and physical sciences that could not otherwise be demonstrated. Motion-picture film, to its credit, was and is easily edited—a desirable characteristic for television or any other application where the recording and playback of visual information is requisite to the daily routine. Existing films, in reference to the early days of television programming, could be edited to fit time slots inside a program, or they could be edited to become a complete time-scheduled program. For time-delay telecasts or for repeat telecasts, recordings on motion-picture film could be made with equipment especially designed for the purpose. Such equipment is still in use at many television installations; it is known as *kinescope* equipment.

To make a kinescope recording, a special motion-picture camera using 16-mm sprocketed film is positioned in front of the screen of a television picture tube (a kinescope). It is possible to photograph the screen of a high-quality monitor in this manner and obtain usable pictures; however, equipment specifically intended for video recording is also available. The system in Fig. 5-1 incorporates a special cathode-ray tube for the display of the television picture and a 16-mm camera (upper right of photo) for photographing the picture. The cathode-ray tube (visible at the upper left portion of the equipment) is operated at an exceptionally high anode potential. This high anode potential provides the high maximum level of brightness essential to the optical system of the equipment. The exposure of the film is controlled by adjusting the brightness of the cathode-ray tube screen. Electronic circuitry may be employed in a kinescope recording system to fulfill the function normally supplied by the camera shutter. Basically, as the film is pulled past the optical system of the camera, the cathode-ray tube is triggered on and off. This eliminates potential problems of synchronism and the irregularities of

Courtesy General Precision, Inc.

Fig. 5-1. A kinescope recording system for television.

exposure that are sometimes encountered with mechanical film shutters and gates. The sound channel is simultaneously recorded on the edge of the 16-mm film as a variable-density track. The audio response of such a system may extend to 7 kilocycles. As with conventional motion-picture film procedures, the kinescoped film must be processed before it can be played back for viewing. For purposes of editing, "work prints" are usually made from the original recording. These prints are edited and assembled, and the final print for projection is made from the "work print." It is, of course, practicable to edit the original film, and project directly from it. This saves costs of film stock for the work print and reduces time lapses by eliminating the need for processing the final print. However, if the final film is to be distributed to other television systems, it is necessary to make duplicate prints.

The major advantage in kinescope recording is that the final film can be shown wherever there is a 16-mm projector, and such equipment is universally available. There are other factors, however, that have caused a decline in the popularity of kinescope recordings. These factors have made the medium of magnetic-tape recording immediately welcome.

Among the major disadvantages inherent in the kinescope recording system is the inability to make instantaneous recordings. Delays of several hours between recording and playback are caused by the inescapable requirement for processing the film. This is an unfortunate inconvenience. It could be of critical importance to be able to play back a video record immediately after it has been put on film while the cast, operating personnel, and sets are still assembled and the experience of the performance is still fresh. At that moment the profit from such a capability would be maximum. Therefore, time delays can become extraordinarily expensive if after the processed film is viewed, it is necessary to reassemble personnel and sets for a retake. In addition, the cost of processing the film must be considered. Once exposed, the film stock cannot be re-used as a medium for a new recording; it is truly permanent. Film wears with use and is easily scratched. Some of the "sharpness" of the original picture becomes lost in the kinescope process. One can usually recognize a kinescoped telecast by virtue of its visual quality. It is unusual to be able to detect a change in the visual image when a magnetic tape is substituted for a live performance.

MAGNETIC TAPE

If magnetic-tape video recording has a serious limitation, at the present time it is the relatively high cost of the recorder

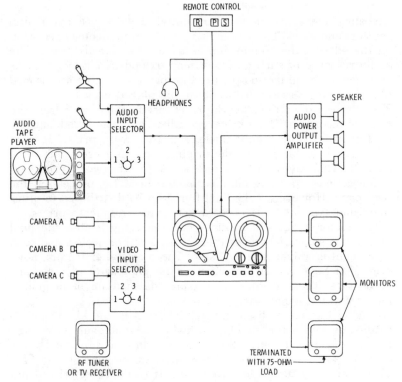

Fig. 5-2. Diagram of typical flexible CCTV system.

mechanism. However, manufacturers are rapidly developing and refining their video tape equipment, reducing costs, and improving performance capabilities. One important factor to consider in regard to the cost of video tape equipment is the fact that no laboratory processing is needed with magnetic tape. In addition, magnetic-tape stock can be erased and recorded many times without incurring new costs for replacement tape. Magnetic-tape records can be played back many times without apparent deterioration in picture quality. Fig. 5-2 shows a highly versatile CCTV magnetic tape system for production and playback of program material.

Video recordings on magnetic tape provide the important benefits of instantaneous playback. As with sound magnetic-tape recordings, playback can take place immediately after the recorded tape is rewound onto the reel from which it was fed during the recording procedure. Picture quality, resolution, gray-scale reproduction, and general "sharpness" are considerably superior to those obtainable with kinescope recording. On the basis of end

Courtesy Ampex Corporation

Fig. 5-3. A modern video tape recorder, with quadrature heads and 2-inch tape.

result alone, magnetic tape is assured a positive position in all fields of television recording, open- and closed-circuit systems included.

The *Videotape* recorder, a name originated by the Ampex Corporation, was first shown at the 1956 Convention of the National Association of Broadcasters. It was intended for commercial TV broadcasts. In fact, at the time, price alone restricted its general use in other phases of television. Fortunately the state of the art has advanced dramatically since 1956. Equipment has been simplified and prices of late models are at levels that put magnetic-tape recording equipment within the reach of all fields using television. A photo of a modern video tape recorder used in broadcast and high-resolution CCTV operations is given in Fig. 5-3.

There are three basic techniques for the recording and playback of video signals on the medium of magnetic tape: (1) longitudinal, (2) helical, and (3) transverse. These are the three which have been made commercially available with varying degrees of success. The first, longitudinal, appears to be the least likely to succeed; in fact, in 1969, several years after commercial offerings made by several companies of longitudinal video tape recorders, it is accurate to report that such units are not being offered for general sale. The second and third techniques are being regularly offered as standard products in regular production by several world-famous companies. Now it is appropriate to describe the three techniques.

Longitudinal Technique

Equipment developed for longitudinal recording and playback at video frequencies resembles equipment intended for audio-frequency use. The recording and playback heads are stationary, fixed in a position that places the head gaps at 90° angles with respect to the linear movement of the tape. The tape travels longitudinally, across the heads. To reduce problems of short wavelengths becoming cancelled by the geometry of the gap of the heads, or, to put it more precisely, to enable signals of short wavelengths to be recorded onto the tape, the tape moves at a speed considerably greater than that used with audio-frequency tape recording equipment. Whereas 7.5 inches per second is a commonly used linear tape speed in professional and home audio-frequency equipment, longitudinal video tape recorders that have been offered for sale have tape speeds of 100 inches per second. As with audio-frequency recording equipment, ¼-inch-width tapes have been used. The picture-making qualities of longitudinal tape recorders, combined with problems in reliability of the tape pulling mechanisms, have contrived to make such equipment unacceptable to the modern, sophisticated user of video tape hardware.

Transverse Technique

In 1956 the video tape recorder demonstrated to the engineering community at the annual convention of the National Association of Broadcasters used 2-inch-wide tape. The subjective quality of the pictures demonstrated to the most sophisticated participants made it clear that video tape was a reality. The technique used was that of transverse recording. This technique is also referred to as *quadrature*. The latter reference is earned by the fact that four heads are used for the video signal. The heads are part of the shaft of a high-speed motor, the axis of which is in line with the direction of the tape travel. The four heads are rotated in a plane that is 90° with respect to the tape direction of travel. Thus the video signal is impressed on the tape as a series of nearly vertical stripes. This is shown in Fig. 5-4. Note that the audio

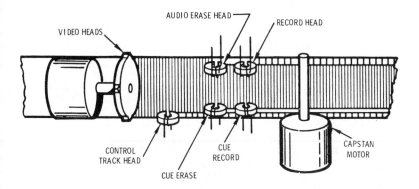

Fig. 5-4. Audio, control, and video tracks on 2-inch tape in quadrature or transverse recording technique.

signal is recorded longitudinally, as is the control track which is used to actuate the capstan-motor servo electronics. Such video tape recorders are supplied with drive mechanisms which move the tape at switchable linear speeds of 7.5 and 15 ips.

Helical Technique

From the standpoint of quantity, there are many more helical-scan video tape recorders in use than either of the other two types discussed. Helical scan is illustrated very basically in Figs. 5-5A and 5-5B. The tape is actually wrapped spirally (helically) around a scanning assembly or drum. Inside the assembly are one or more video heads mounted on the shaft of a high-speed motor. The tips of the video heads project through a slit in the skin of the drum so that the tips do physically contact the magnetic-tape oxide surface. Unlike the transverse technique, the rotating direction of the heads is in the plane of tape travel. However, because the tape is helically wound around the drum, the track of video information is laid down as a series of diagonal stripes (Fig. 5-6). Helical-scan video tape recorders have been produced that use ½-inch-, 1-inch- and 2-inch-wide magnetic tape. The first commercially available, quantity-produced helical-scan units used 2-inch tape, the same as for the transverse or quadrature-head tape recorders. There is no published standard for helical-scan tape widths; it is entirely at the discretion of the owner/operator to make his choice. Tapes recorded on a "½-inch" machine will not play back on a "1-" or "2-inch" machine. Also, helically scanned 2-inch tape will not play back on a transversely scanned machine. Manufacturers do claim that tapes are interchangeable from machine to machine of the same type, i.e., 1-inch to 1-inch.

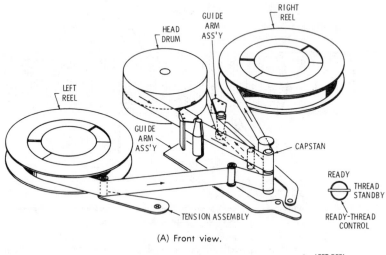

(A) Front view.

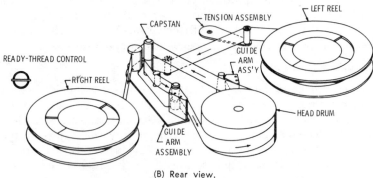

(B) Rear view.

Fig. 5-5. Spiral tape path used in helical-scan recorders.

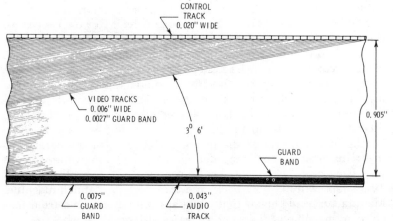

Fig. 5-6. Audio, control, and video tracks used in helical-scan technique.

In some helically scanned units, the length of an individual stripe of video signal is approximately 10 inches. With a track width in the order of only 0.006 inch, it becomes apparent that precision tolerances must be maintained in guiding the tape through its path, including the wrap around the "skin" of the scanning assembly. Although universal standards have not been established for helical-scan equipment, *de facto* "standards" have arisen as a result of practice. Many broadcast operators have adopted 2-inch transverse- and 2-inch helical-scan equipment for use directly on the air. One-inch helical scan has been finding increasing acceptance in education and medicine, possibly because of the reduced costs of the medium. Half-inch helical-scan equipment is finding acceptance in places such as the home and small business where reduced picture resolution may be tolerated, and low costs and one-of-a-kind equipment are needed.

Audio and control tracks are longitudinally recorded as with transversely scanned equipment on the edges of the tape. Full-track erase capabilities are provided so that with one pass all signals can be removed from the tape, wiping it "clean," so to speak. Some helical-scan tape equipment has provision for dual audio-track recording so that a commentary can be added along with the originally synchronized audio. It is common practice among manufacturers of such equipment to enable the audio to be completely controlled separately without affecting the video; that is, an audio track may be separately erased or recorded with or without video. At least one manufacturer in 1969 manufactured and marketed a portable helical-scan video tape recorder and camera as a unit. The time capability is about 20 minutes. The tape must be played back on a separate but compatible player. The "recorder" contains no playback facilities. The camera is a vidicon type.

PORTABLE TV TAPE RECORDERS

When magnetic tape recorders for sound were physically reduced to make them portable, new concepts of radio programs and commercial records were developed. Exciting approaches to the preservation of sound became feasible. The progression of magnetic tape recorders for sound was from fixed, bolted-down models, through transportable "suitcase" units, to "memobook" battery-powered portables. It is probable that magnetic tape equipment for TV recordings is now undergoing a similar metamorphosis. At present, we are at the relative "suitcase" stage of transportability, as exemplified by the unit pictured in Fig. 5-7. It is exciting to contemplate some of the applications for such equipment, as ownership and utility capabilities are increased.

Courtesy Precision Instrument Co.

Fig. 5-7. A portable TV tape recorder.

Mobile TV trucks have been used by all classes of television operations for many years. The sight of a large van parked outside a building, with numerous large-diameter cables running to and from the van and the building, is familiar to many. The question in most observers' minds was whether the building was "feeding" the van, or the van was "servicing" the building. However, if you looked closely, a long heavy cable running from the van up the side of the building to the roof was usually observed. The "dish" and "black box" of a microwave transmitter were placed on the roof. Effectively, because the roof-top equipment provides the link between remote location and the "home base" of the van, all of the cables, the cameras, and the control equipment inside the van that generated the synchronizing signals terminated at that roof top. Lacking convenient intracity coaxial cables, or being denied access to such cables, the station engineers found the microwave link often the most practical way of sending the picture from the remote location to the TV station. At the TV station the picture received on a microwave receiver would be fed to a TV tape recorder console.

For a spot pickup or a brief interview, it was often impractical to transport an entire crew and van to the remote location. The alternate and frequently used choice for picture coverage has been to send a cameraman with portable 16-mm motion-picture film equipment (tripod mounted or hand held). The limitations of this approach are adequately described in the first part of this chapter. True, there are many times when motion-picture cameras are the best choice as the medium for recording pictures for telecasting purposes. For example, in TV-newsreel work and candid photography in situations demanding complete mobility of equipment and personnel, the total independence from "umbilical" power cables permitted by 16-mm film cameras is often essential.

TV tape recorders depend on TV cameras for their optics and conversion of the visual image to electrical impulses. Image orthicon or vidicon TV cameras fulfill this function with TV tape recorders. A complete system for a TV tape recording chain retains the "umbilical" cord requirement that ties the TV cameraman to sources of power and to the recording terminal. The metamorphosis is taking place, however. New equipment is commercially available that may signal a revolution in techniques for mobility of the cameraman and the eventual elimination of the film photographer. The equipment consists of a miniature hand-held vidicon camera, and a back-pack microwave transmitter. The "pack," worn by the cameraman, contains a battery supply for power, the transmitter, and a miniature nondirectional antenna. The only cable involved is the one connecting the camera to the back pack. Complete mobility is afforded, just as with a motion-picture film camera setup. Such innovations as this become especially significant with the commercial availability of the "suitcase" TV tape recorder operated from inside a compact automobile (Fig. 5-8). Parked within the general area of the "back-pack" TV cameraman and fitted with a compatible microwave receiver, this automobile provides an instantaneous recording system in a highly mobile package. The arrival of the "suitcase" TV tape recorder is a giant step important to all operators of closed-circuit television systems.

Now, instead of a giant van, the mobile TV unit can be installed in a compact automobile. Instead of microwaving the pictures back to the TV station or leasing coaxial cables to the TV station from the remote location, the pictures can be recorded on magnetic tape at the scene of action. When the action is mobile, the TV camera and the magnetic tape recorder can "race" alongside, taping all the way. If necessary, the mobile unit can be racing back to the TV station while the tape is being rewound. This type of installation is especially attractive to location recording for TV commercials (Fig. 5-9). But, more important, it is an ideal arrangement for an educational closed-circuit TV system, for "photographing" field trips and documentaries, a travelogue for a

Courtesy Ampex Corporation

Fig. 5-8. A compact station wagon equipped with remote-TV recording facilities.

Courtesy Ampex Corporation

Fig. 5-9. A typical application for a mobile TV recording unit.

history or geography class, and industrial scenes for classes in economics. The high mobility of such an installation, free of power lines and long cables, enables TV recordings to be made in normally inaccessible places while retaining the high picture quality that is characteristic of magnetic tape. No doubt the "transportable" TV tape recorder will find a permanent place in the television scene. In planning the closed-circuit TV system it is advisable to plan floor space for at least one TV tape recorder. If budgetary considerations restrict the immediate acquisition of this equipment, do not discount its future addition. It is possible that such equipment will reach the relative low price and utility of today's magnetic-tape sound equipment.

Typical Portable TV Tape Recorder

In the mid-1960's Ampex introduced a series of video tape recorders intended primarily for the educational/industrial user who was not necessarily concerned with putting his taped material "on the air" but was concerned more with closed-circuit applications to a known viewing audience. The series is designated "VR." The units in the series are intended to be transportable and are provided with integral carrying cases and handles. Because all units in the series are derived from one basic design it is well to become familiar with one: the VR-5100 (Fig. 5-10).

Courtesy Ampex Corporation

Fig. 5-10. Ampex VR-5100 video tape record/playback unit.

Description of VR-5100—This recorder is intended for industrial, educational, hospital, and home use. Picture quality is comparable to, or better than, that of a standard television receiver. The specifications of the unit are given in Fig. 5-11.

SPECIFICATIONS

POWER REQUIREMENTS
105 to 125 volts, 60 cycle at 2-1/2 amps.
Detachable 3-wire power cable and plug.

VIDEO INPUT REAR PANEL SWITCH SELECTS:
Either UHF connector or remote connector. Both connectors are 75 ohms, unbalanced, terminated internally.

VIDEO OUTPUT
75 ohms unbalanced, .8V P-P Min. (EE or Play). UHF type connector.

MODULATOR OUTPUT
Video modulated radio frequency output. UHF type connector.
Tuneable through channels 2 to 5 for use with standard TV receiver, Recorder preset to Channel 4.
Nominal output 30 millivolts into 75 ohm load. Connects to TV receiver antenna terminals.

AUDIO INPUT REAR PANEL SWITCH SELECTS:

Input	Sensitivity (100% Record level)	Impedance
Microphone	1.5 MV.	80K ohms
Line	80 MV.	47K ohms
Remote	80 MV.	47K ohms

Microphone and line inputs use an XL type connector.

AUDIO OUTPUTS
1. 10K ohm unbalanced line. 1.0 volt nominal output. XL type connector.
2. 8 ohm, 2 watts nominal feeding internal speaker. Available externally at speaker jack.

VIDEO RESPONSE
30 HZ to 3.0 MHZ +2, −6db with reference to 0.5 MHZ

VIDEO SIGNAL TO NOISE
42db, Peak-to-Peak signal to RMS noise.

HORIZONTAL RESOLUTION
300 lines limiting visual resolution on monoscope test pattern.

AUDIO RESPONSE
±4db, 90 HZ to 9 KHZ.

AUDIO SIGNAL TO NOISE
39db from peak record level.

AUDIO FLUTTER AND WOW
Flutter: less than .3% RMS .5-250 HZ
Measured according to ASA Standards
Wow: less than .04% RMS .5-6 HZ

TAPE SPEED
9.62 ips, ±1%.

VIDEO WRITING SPEED
1000 ips.

ROTARY HEAD LIFE
500 hrs. minimum when used with Ampex tape.
Will require adjustment after 250 hrs.
Uses a single plug-in field interchangeable head.

REWIND TIME
5 minutes (for 3000 ft. of tape).

FAST FORWARD TIME
5 minutes (for 3000 ft. of tape).

REMOTE CONTROL FACILITY
Remote control connections available for play, record and stop at back panel for use with remote control device or Ampex CC6455 camera.

TAPE
1" wide, 1 mil mylar base video tape.
2950 ft. for 1 hr. recording time on 9-3/4" reel.

CASE
Vinyl clad sheet aluminum with die cast end frames incorporating swing-out handles, removable dust cover is of similar construction.

SIZE
Overall 23-1/4" × 18-1/4" × 12-1/2"

WEIGHT
62 lbs.

OPERATING POSITION
Horizontal only.

Courtesy Ampex Corporation

Fig. 5-11. Specifications for Ampex VR-5100.

A minimum number of controls makes it extremely easy to operate; a video camera, video line, or audio line source may be used. Full interchangeability with all Ampex recorders using this format is guaranteed by the manufacturer. Stop motion is available to permit examination of single frames.

Head life is 500 hours, with an adjustment required after 250 hours. Plug-in head characteristics make it possible to provide field replacements with a minimum of adjustments. Maintenance is further simplified by the wrap-around case design that allows removal by simply unscrewing the rubber bumpers that serve as the legs for the cabinet.

A maximum recording time of 60 minutes is provided by a 2950-foot reel of 1-inch videotape. An air film is developed between the rotating drum and recording tape which reduces friction in the tape loop.

Two video outputs are provided. One is a composite video output for use with a standard closed-circuit monitor, and the other is a modulated RF output that can be connected to the antenna terminals of a conventional television receiver. Fig. 5-12 shows the connector panel at the rear of the unit. The modulated RF output is preset to Channel 4 at the factory but is adjustable to Channels 2 through 5.

In addition to the mechanical system, three essential elements are required for recording and reproducing: the recording medium, the recording circuits, and the reproducing circuits. The recording medium is tape. The tape consists of two parts: the base and the magnetic coating.

The base is usually cellulose acetate or polyester plastic. Physical properties—playing time, strength, smoothness, curl, twist, stickiness, print through, and deterioration time—are determined by the base.

The magnetic coating consists of iron oxide particles, which are needle shaped and lie in a lengthwise direction on the tape. A binder material holds the particles in place, and makes the particles adhere to the base. This material determines the tape's magnetic properties—frequency response, sensitivity, distortion and signal-to-noise ratio. The surface of the oxide coating is highly polished to minimize wear of the heads, and to improve the contact between the tape surface and head gap.

Magnetization results because of the existence of magnetic islands or tiny sectional magnets (domains) in the material. In an unmagnetized state there is complete disorder of these areas with mutual cancellation between the domains: the remaining field is almost zero. When an external field is applied to the tape, the individual domains tend to magnetically align along the axis of the field. The number that align is dependent on the strength of the applied field.

The length of the sectional magnets depends on the tape speed and the frequency of the magnetizing field. For high-frequency signals the magnets are short and lie closer to the surface of the

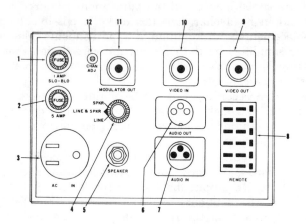

1. Fuse: 1 Amp Slo-Blo

2. Fuse: 5 Ampere

3. AC Power Receptacle:

4. Audio Output Selector:
   LINE position supplies +4dbm into 600 ohm balanced or unbalanced line.
   LINE and SPKR position supplies +4dbm nominally into 600 ohm line in addition to providing internal speaker with audio.
   SPKR position gives internal speaker output only.

5. SPEAKER: Connects to external speakers. This output is controlled by Audio Output Selector.

6. AUDIO OUTPUT: Supplies audio to a balanced or unbalanced 600 ohm line. Output is controlled by Audio Output Selector.

7. AUDIO INPUT: Microphone or audio line is connected here. Impedance for microphone is 200 ohms. Impedances for line is 100K, balanced bridging. Input level for microphone is .2mv minimum. Input level for line is .12 to 4.9 volts.

8. REMOTE: Provides remote control facility. The dummy plug is removed and connector from remote control is inserted into 18 pin connector. NOTE: The front panel pushbuttons will not function properly if a connector or the dummy plug is not inserted into the 18 pin connector.

9. VIDEO OUTPUT: Connects to TV monitor or modified receiver. Output level from recording made at 100% level is 1 volt peak to peak into 75 ohm video cables.

10. VIDEO INPUT: Connects to video output of a TV camera or TV monitor. Requires 1 volt peak to peak composite video to give 100% record level.

11. MODULATOR OUTPUT: Connects to television receiver antenna terminals. Provides approximately 30mv for tv channels 2 through 5. See below.

12. CHANNEL ADJ: Adjusts the carrier frequency of the MODULATOR OUTPUT for channels 2 through 5. To adjust, set television receiver to desired channel (2-5) and center TV fine tuning. Then using a slotted plastic tool, adjust CHAN ADJ for best picture on receiver.

Courtesy Ampex Corporation

Fig. 5-12. VR-5100 connector panel shows simplicity of connection to and from other elements of CCTV system.

oxide. Thus, for a constant tape speed the length of the sectional magnets varies inversely with the frequency of the signal.

In the magnetic recorder the field patterns are generated by the record head. The record head consists of a number of turns of wire to form a magnetic loop on a highly permeable core material with a small gap. When recording or reproducing, the oxide surface of the tape contacts the gap in the core, thus completing the magnetic circuit through the tape surface. During the recording process, the current through the coil varies, and the sectional magnets within the oxide surface are aligned according to the direction and intensity of the record signal. Signal amplitude increases the intensity and the direction of head current determines the polarity. As the frequency increases, the spacing between the maximum-intensity points decreases. In short, the recorded pattern on the surface of the tape resembles a series of tiny magnets that vary in polarity and density.

The process is reversed when reproducing. As the tape passes the gap in the play head, the magnetic circuit is completed and a voltage that is proportional to the rate of magnetic change is induced in the winding of the head. When the wavelength of the sectional magnets on the oxide equals the width of the gap, the rate of change becomes zero and induces no voltage. This is called the *cutoff frequency;* those frequencies above this range are not reproduced dependably. There are four other factors that contribute to the high-frequency limitation. These are: recording demagnetization, self-demagnetization, penetration losses, and head losses. As pointed out previously, the reproduce head output increases with frequency up to a point and then decreases rapidly to zero. This gap effect is the most serious single restriction on the high-frequency response of the recorder. Fig. 5-13 provides a graphical representation of the gap effect. From the illustration it can be seen that a constant-current recording of the full frequency range at a given tape speed will produce an increasing output voltage up to a point and then rapidly drop to zero. This sudden dropoff of output is characteristic of all tape recorders and limits the number of octaves that can be effectively reproduced to approximately 10.

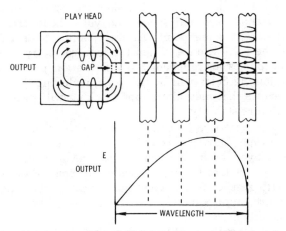

Fig. 5-13. Gap effect determines minimum tape speed to achieve wide-band frequency response.

To summarize: The bandwidth that can be reproduced on magnetic tape is limited to approximately 10 octaves by the nature of the reproducing system, and the maximum frequency that can be reproduced is determined by the reproduce gap width and tape speed.

Because a television signal extends from near DC to 3.5 megacycles, a bandwidth of almost 18 octaves, a method is required to transform the signal to a higher-frequency spectrum and yet maintain the information contained in the original signal. This is achieved by converting the television signals to frequency modulated signals.

After the highest playback frequency is determined and the minimum practical head gap established, the necessary tape speed can be calculated. The derived head-to-tape velocity for the required bandwidth is 1000 inches per second.

Single-Head Helical-Scan Format—One video record/play head is utilized to record one field per scan or rotation of the drum. A drum speed of 3600 rpm is required because the drum rotation must follow each occurring field every 1/60 second. The effective recorded tape length is based on the drum circumference, which can be calculated by dividing 60 (fields) into one. Multiplying this figure by the 1000-ips writing speed (required for proper frequency response) gives an effective length of 16.6 inches. The drum diameter then becomes 16.6 inches divided by π (3.14), or 5.3 inches.

Because the video and sync pulses are recorded on the tape in a series of parallel diagonal tracks, the 9.6-inch longitudinal tape speed is required so that the horizontal sync pulses will line up from one track to the next. During slow motion, or speeds other than the original recorded speed, the video head crosses from track to track at some point. At this point signals from both tracks will be read at once. When the tape geometry is arranged so that the pulses are aligned, the information picked up from the two adjoining fields will be the same, including the sync timing. Any errors that may affect tape tracking will thus have less effect on picture stability.

As the tape enters, the head passes a point where it does not contact the tape. During this period, no information can be recorded or played back. This short absence of signal when the head does not contact the tape is called *dropout*. Position of the dropout with respect to the television signal is near the bottom of the picture, approximately two lines before the start of the vertical blanking.

Functional Operation—When the switch is turned on in the play mode, power is applied to the circuit boards and the drive

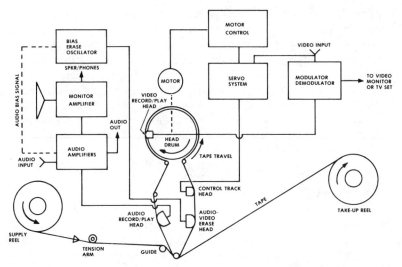

Courtesy Ampex Corporation

Fig. 5-14. VR-5100 electronic and mechanical systems.

motors. The head drum motor also rotates because the motor control amplifier is energized. However, there is no tape motion unless the ready-thread knob is in the ready position and the play button is depressed.

When the ready-thread knob is in the ready position and the play button is depressed, the tape moves out from the supply reel over the tension arm, tape guides, and capstan to the video/audio erase head (Fig. 5-14). This head does not function in the play mode. After the tape passes the erase head it is guided over the control track head. The output from the control track head is fed to the servo system for video head positioning information and correction of the motor speed. The output from the servo system is fed to the motor control amplifier, which in turn operates the drum motor, increasing and decreasing the speed as required.

The tape motion is then guided around the head drum in an angular loop. The bottom section of the drum is stationary while the upper half rotates at 3600 rpm. The video play head is attached to the upper drum and thus rotates with it. The tape wrap (angular loop) provides the proper recording and play angle as explained previously.

Signals from the video head are coupled to a preamplifier through a rotary transformer. The output from the preamplifier in turn is coupled to a demodulator. The demodulated output couples to a jack on the rear panel, and then to a TV monitor or a modified TV set.

From the head drum the tape motion continues past the audio head where the variations of the magnetic field induce an audio signal into the play head. The audio signal is coupled to an audio amplifier and monitor amplifier. The output of the monitor amplifier feeds an internal speaker, or an external speaker when using the SPKR/PHONES jack. A line from the audio amplifier connects to the jack on the rear panel for connecting the output to an external amplifier. The tape motion continues over the capstan roller to the take-up reel, which revolves in a clockwise direction.

Transport operation and tape motion remains the same in the record mode. However, circuit operation does change, and signal tracing is different. The bias oscillator, which was inoperative in the play mode, is now active. As the tape passes the erase head any previous recorded material is erased. A portion of the oscillator signal is fed to the audio amplifier for biasing. The control track head is energized, and it records a control signal on the tape. The video input signal is frequency modulated before it is fed to the video record head. The audio signal is amplified by the audio amplifier and coupled to the audio record head. This completes the record operation.

Video Tape Electronics—Electronic components described include those associated with the signal system, the head-drum servo system, the power supplies, the video control track, erase oscillator, and the audio system.

Modulator and Demodulator Circuit Function—The modulator and demodulator are separate video signal processing circuits. Incoming video signals are converted to FM so that they can be recorded on tape. This function is necessary because the recorder cannot process the extreme frequency range of the video signal without converting it to FM.

Conversion is achieved through the use of the frequency modulation circuitry. Modulation is determined by the signal level delivered to the circuit. In operation the modulator is adjusted for a certain frequency, which is changed by the various levels of the incoming video signals. For example, whenever the input signal level corresponds to the blanking level, the modulator is operating at 4 mc. As the input moves to peak white level, the frequency rises to 5.5 mc. On the other hand, as the input level goes down to the tips of the synchronizing pulses, the frequency decreases to 3.5 mc.

In the record mode the modulator output is amplified and fed to the rotating head, which varies the magnetic field of the tape accordingly. A portion of the signal (E-E signal) is fed to the demodulator so that the demodulated signal can be coupled to the TV monitor for observing the output.

Video signals fed directly to the frequency modulator (without pre-emphasis) produce an objectionable amount of high-frequency noise. The eye is very sensitive to these signals, which would be included in the recorded signal.

To prevent this noise from being seen, the higher frequencies of the video signal are pre-emphasized by a network during the record mode. When the tape is played, a circuit with inverse characteristics in the demodulator returns the video signal back to normal, and at the same time reduces the high-frequency noise that is introduced during recording.

In the play mode, the magnetic orientation of the tape induces a video signal into the play head. The recorded signal recovered from the tape is about one millivolt. At this point the main advantage of the FM conversion becomes apparent. Amplitude changes cannot affect the output because the information is recorded as frequency. As a result, the tape can be saturated during record without the nonlinear amplitude distortion when the tape is played. The play signal is fed through the limiter circuits to make it independent of input amplitude changes. The limiters remove any unwanted amplitude modulation that may be introduced by the tape irregularities and variable spacing between the head and tape.

The output from the limiter feeds a frequency demodulator; in the demodulator the modulation process is reversed and the signal is recovered.

Meter Circuit Function—The meter provides two distinct functions: (1) It indicates signal level when recording, and (2) it provides tracking indication during playback. In playback the modulated RF is coupled from the preamplifier to the meter driver stage. Any small signal variations are bypassed to maintain a constant current to the meter. In playback the maximum RF is obtained when the head is tracking properly and is indicated by a maximum indication on the meter.

Dropout Circuit Function—The dropout circuit suppresses any noise that may be present when no RF information is being received from the tape. If the output is not clamped, noise could trigger the sync circuits of the video monitor.

Servo Circuit Function—The servo circuit is necessary to control the operation of the drum motor. A control track is recorded during the record mode to provide a reference of head position with respect to the video signal. Two inputs are supplied to the servo amplifier in the record mode: (1) tachometer pulses and (2) vertical sync pulses. The tac pulses are used as a reference for head position, and vertical pulses are used as a reference for the location of the video signal. Each line of video that is played back must start in the proper position to provide a stable picture without streaks or tears.

Two inputs are also supplied to the servo amplifier during the play mode: tachometer pulses and the control track signal. A varying DC voltage is developed to correct the motor speed so that the head will be located in the proper position in relation to the pulses.

Bias and Erase Oscillator Function—The servo board houses the erase oscillator circuit. Oscillator operation occurs when the unit is placed in video/audio record. A bias signal at 67 kc is supplied to the audio record head.

Video Head Driver and RF Preamplifier Circuit Function—During the record/standby and record mode the head driver circuit receives FM information from the modulator circuit and amplifies this signal for use by the video head, which is located in the rotating drum. An FM signal is also fed back to the demodulator from the head driver. This is the E-to-E signal that is routed through the system to permit a performance test of the circuit functions without the use of a tape. During play operation the signal induced in the video head is coupled to the RF preamplifier. This circuit amplifies and equalizes the signal to be fed to the demodulator for playback.

Monitor Amplifier Circuit Function—The monitor amplifier receives an audio signal from the audio board and converts it to an adequate power level for driving a speaker.

Power-Supply Circuit Function—Two basic power supplies are employed to provide the DC voltages for operating all of the circuits of the recorder and the drum motor. The transformer and rectifiers of one supply make up one subassembly. This supply furnishes the operating voltage for the monitor amplifier and the motor control amplifier. This same transformer provides the energy for the second supply, which is located on a separate subassembly. The other supply provides +18, −12, and +12 volts, and is controlled by a section on the modulator-demodulator board.

Care of Video Recording Tape

Magnetic tape is a strong permanent recording medium, unaffected by ordinary handling or storage. However, it should be kept away from heat, moisture, and other magnetic materials. Avoid stretching the tape, or you will distort and destroy the quality of the recording. You should also avoid contact with the oxide surface of the tape, because fingerprints or other contamination of oxide surface may cause the video head to clog (oxide buildup on surface of head) and result in loss of signal during recording or playback.

Making Copies of Recordings

Copies of TV tapes are referred to by "generation." The original is the "first generation." A copy made from the original TV tape is called a "second-generation tape." The quality of the second generation is remarkably good; it is difficult to distinguish from the picture produced on a TV monitor fed by the original, or first generation. A copy of a second-generation tape is called the "third generation." At this point in making copies the picture reproduction capabilities begin to deteriorate rapidly. The quality at the third generation becomes comparable to a kinescope recording on 16-mm film. It is obviously desirable to use the first-generation TV tape for telecasting. Commercial-TV stations make two first-generation tapes simultaneously to provide a "safety tape." Should one of the originals become damaged, lost, or destroyed, the duplicate first-generation tape can be used. However, closed-circuit television installations are usually not equipped with enough TV tape recorders to enable this practice to be followed. Therefore, as soon as possible, a copy of the original should be recorded. Thus, the second-generation tape becomes the safety for the first-generation tape, the latter being used for the actual telecast. In making copies of TV tapes, the audio as well as the picture track is copied automatically.

Closed-Circuit Television
in Education

THE VARIOUS COMPONENTS that are assembled to become a closed-circuit television system have been described in the previous chapters. From the basic single camera and monitor setup, we have moved deliberately and progressively through many of the commercial accessories intended to increase the usefulness of the system. Up to this point we have considered purely hypothetical circumstances under which closed-circuit television can play a useful role. The general benefits of closed-circuit television have been pointed out in these situations. All is not "make believe" in considering ways and means to use or apply such systems. There are a great number of closed-circuit television systems in operation today, and the number is increasing rapidly as more and more organizations become acquainted with the advantages offered by CCTV systems.

Every installation is planned to fulfill a specific set of requirements and to satisfy specific needs. These needs may include the enhancement of human performance, the reduction of human error, the substitution of human performers, or the safety of personnel and the security of persons, places, and things.

EDUCATIONAL OR INSTRUCTIONAL TELEVISION

The terms "educational television" and "instructional television" are often used interchangeably. However, there are differences in their primary purposes that make them separate. The sophisticated teacher and student have become very much aware of those differences. So, too, is the layman developing such an awareness. The dissimilarities of educational television (ETV) and of instructional television (ITV) are basic.

If the primary purpose of the material being telecast is to enhance the viewer's knowledge and general understanding of a subject *without* giving credits that may be applied to the earning of a diploma or a degree, the term "educational television" correctly applies. On the other hand, if the telecast is part of a formalized schedule of educational broadcasts that are transmitted on a planned schedule, and from which formal examinations and scholastic credits are earned, the correct description is "instructional television." The former is informal, while the latter is directed to a specific viewing group. Both make excellent use of closed-circuit television. The technique of teaching, or learning, via television is becoming increasingly popular. In many communities open-circuit transmissions are being made through local cooperating commercial TV stations and through noncommercial educational TV stations. The telecasts are announced in the press, and anyone with a TV set can tune in. In closed-circuit ETV and ITV, announcements and viewers are restricted to participants within the system.

CLASSROOM INSTRUCTION

Intramural TV exchanges take place among school systems to the mutual benefit of all parties. The exchange of material may be in the form of video tapes, kinescope recordings, or live instructors. Such an exchange is highly attractive to serious educators who recognize that unusual talents can be found among teachers who have developed specialties in teaching, and who communicate well through the medium of closed-circuit television. For example, a school that is fortunate enough to have a "Miss Jones" with her special abilities in teaching English II can, through live television or recorded media, extend an invitation to the entire school district to share in the benefits offered by her talents. Too, Miss Jones can be shared with all sessions of the school to which she is assigned—an advantage that would otherwise become a physical impossibility. Other schools within the district or closed-circuit television system can reciprocate by programming their best teachers. Whether "live" or by recordings, all students can enjoy the benefits of high-level instruction.

Televised instruction is always coordinated with the day's curricula so that transitions from television to classroom instructor are natural. This makes the lessons more dynamic and exciting to the classroom as a group. The use of closed-circuit television does not diminish in any way the importance of the classroom instructor. What happens is a change in teaching technique that, if it does affect the value of the classroom instructor, can be considered to make the classroom instructor even more valuable than before.

The use of closed-circuit television in education relieves the classroom instructor of much of the tedium of lesson preparation. The objective of the TV instructor is to dramatize and visually demonstrate those elements of the subject that lend themselves to the medium. For example, the experiments for a biology or physics lab session can be carried out on a larger scale, and the experiments can be made more comprehensive than they could be if conducted every time a class came to session. Having conducted the experiments via television, the program ends and classroom attention returns to the individual instructor within the classroom who continues the lesson. Because of the relative relief from preparation as well as the fact that he is physically within the classroom, he can give more personalized instruction to students assigned to him than he could prior to the advent of closed-circuit classroom television.

Usually the classroom instructor is provided with an advance copy of the TV script so that he can coordinate classroom activity with the TV instructor's telecast, picking up easily where the latter leaves off.

It is interesting to note statistical reports which indicate a reason for the dramatic growth of ETV and ITV. In 1945-1946, public school enrollment was 23,300,000. By 1959-1960, it had risen to 36,000,000. The projection of the U.S. Office of Education for 1969-1970 is 44,500,000. In many school systems there is a severe shortage of classrooms. Many new classrooms are needed to relieve overcrowding and others are needed to replace obsolete facilities. To maintain the current teacher-student ratio in 1969 it is estimated that a third of all college students would have to start their higher education with the intent of becoming teachers. During the 25-year span from 1945 to 1970, the annual cost per student will have risen from $120 to $465. Total annual expenses will have risen from $3 billion to $20 billion.

The ability of a closed-circuit television system to help compensate for the teacher shortages and to provide an eventual reduction in cost per student is being recognized by school officials, governments, teachers, and students. Many are already benefitting from closed-circuit television, many more will in the near future.

Each school must, of course, determine for itself how it is affected by this national picture of growing enrollments, increasing costs, and fewer teachers. Each school must make the following self-examination:

1. What are its current and projected teacher/student ratios?
2. How many students are in each class? Are the classes overcrowded?
3. How adequate is the curriculum in view of modern living?
4. How adequate are the current physical facilities?
5. What additional facilities are required?
6. Does the budget allow for additional teachers, either to relieve the present load or to enable expansion of the curriculum?

An indication that many schools are finding at least partial answers to these questions through the medium of TV classrooms is given with the following statistics compiled in 1961:

1. Approximately 7,500 elementary and secondary schools in 600 school districts were offering at least part of their regular curriculum over television.
2. About 3,000,000 students were attending classes using ITV, with another 3,000,000 being reached by ETV.
3. 250,000 college and university students were attending credit courses on television.
4. 1,000 courses were offered for credits on ITV.
5. 350 closed-circuit television systems were already in operation, with many more under construction or in the planning stage.

APPLICATIONS

Although our data and statistics have been concerned with schools, colleges, and universities which give diplomas and degrees, there are other organizations, of course, concerned with training in individual skills. Among these are included therapeutics, highly specialized courses of instruction, commercial schools, and business organizations that offer training to employees who must either acquire or expand on certain skills and capabilities. Among these various activities there are many that make excellent use of closed-circuit television installations.

In a single classroom, a camera and a monitor in conjunction with a microscope will provide enlargement of the image and enable all students and the instructor to "look through the eyepiece" at the same time. The extraordinary benefits of simul-

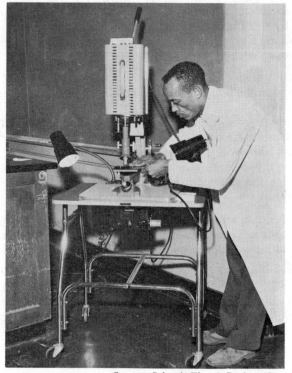

Courtesy Sylvania Electric Products, Inc.

Fig. 6-1. A portable unit consisting of a TV camera, lights, and microscope mounted on a table on wheels for moving from classroom to classroom.

taneous experience as well as the elimination of the student lineup at the microscope are quite obvious. A typical "mobile" setup is shown at Fig. 6-1.

A visiting dignitary (Fig. 6-2) can address an entire school body via closed-circuit television without disrupting the physical school body. This is especially true when all classrooms are equipped with classroom TV monitors. In addition, by making a video tape recording of the message, students who are unable to "attend" the live broadcast can view the presentation later. A rare work of art can be brought to the studio and televised to the classrooms (Fig. 6-3). Motion pictures can be shown via closed-circuit television without darkening the classroom. In addition, the time-consuming handling of film and the projector noise within the classrooms are eliminated.

Panel discussions and seminars can be attended by students throughout the campus. Dramatic arts students can practice their skills under actual studio conditions and, if video tape is part of the facility, can see themselves on the screen minutes after completion of the performance. This type of training is an exceptionally valuable aid to self-improvement. Excerpts, either read or dramatized by a student or instructor, from famous works of literature can give new life to history and language courses. A broadcast of current events can be viewed via television in the history classroom. Music soloists or large concert orchestras can be "fitted" into every music appreciation classroom. Children in play therapy can be unobtrusively observed by therapists in training. Law schools, by special consent of the court, are sometimes permitted to have cameras in actual courtrooms with monitors located in the classroom. In the classroom, the instructor explains the techniques and guides the evaluation of the courtroom dialogues. Medical and dental schools use television to demonstrate diagnostic and surgical techniques (Fig. 6-4). Exceptional closeup views can be provided by the camera.

The Autonetics Division of North American Aviation has used closed-circuit television in a specialized training program for production-line employees. Cameras were placed in the "white rooms" where demonstrations were telecast of inspection techniques used in the production of miniature high-reliability electronic components. Closed-circuit television provided group viewing through the microscopes and enabled closeup views of manual operations that, if done in person, would have been physically impracticable from a time standpoint.

Fig. 6-2. A school official addressing the entire student body without requiring them to leave their classrooms.

Courtesy Precision Instrument Co.

Lindenhurst High School, Suffolk County, New York, uses a basic closed-circuit system to provide visual support for classes in home economics. Great Bridge and Churchland Elementary Schools in Norfolk, Virginia, use television (Fig. 6-5) to receive local open-circuit ETV and closed-circuit ITV. They produce

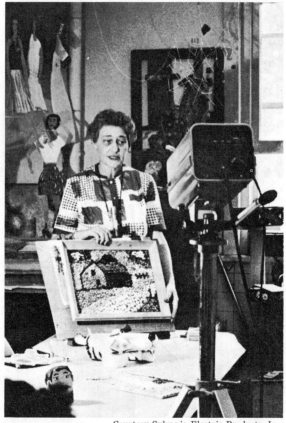

Courtesy Sylvania Electric Products, Inc.

Fig. 6-3. A work of art being shown via CCTV to several classrooms.

many of their own live and filmed programs. Many assembly programs are telecast to individual classrooms to eliminate the need for moving students to and from classrooms and auditoriums. At Southern Illinois University, prior to the full-scale implementation of teaching via television, experiments were made in the feasibility of closed-circuit television in science classrooms. A camera equipped with wide-angle, normal, and telephoto lenses, all turret-mounted, provided enlarged pictures of objects on a 23-inch monitor. Batavia, New York, Junior-Senior High School has used closed-circuit television to accommodate overflow guests at commencement exercises. The arrangement is shown in Fig. 6-6.

The departments of speech and drama at state teachers' colleges use closed-circuit television in training future teachers in classroom conduct and performance. A class in theatrical makeup at

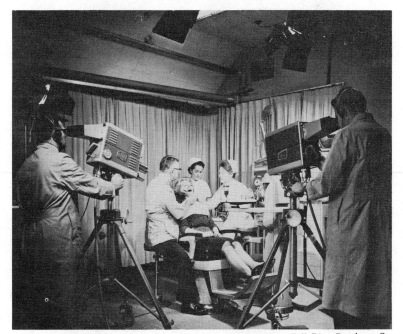

Courtesy Dage-Bell Div., Raytheon Co.

Fig. 6-4. Closed-circuit television in use at the College of Dentistry at the University of Illinois.

Morehead State College, Kentucky, which was ordinarily limited to a half-dozen students, accommodates several dozen simultaneously with the aid of a camera and monitor (Fig. 6-7). The same college uses television to enable student teachers to observe the dramatic play of children under the guidance of a skilled instructor. Because they are separated from the children, the student teachers do not cause the distraction that would result if they were in the same room.

Experimentally, a special local rule was passed permitting the circuit judge in Washtenaw County Circuit Court, Ann Arbor, Michigan, to allow the use of live-television transmission via closed-circuit system for the benefit of law students at the University of Michigan Law School. It was allowed to assist the university faculty in demonstrating courtroom techniques in special classrooms that were declared as adjunct courtrooms. Remote control in the classrooms enabled the camera to be zoomed, panned, tilted, and focused. This technique enabled the

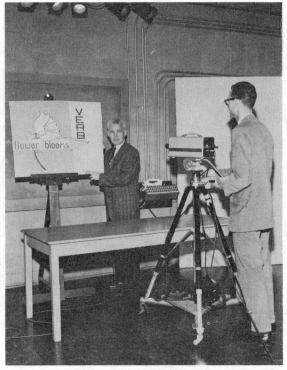

Courtesy Sylvania Electric Products, Inc.

Fig. 6-5. A live program at Norfolk, Virginia.

students and faculty to discuss the proceedings of the court without disturbing the court. Sound, of course, was simultaneously transmitted. The judge could "clear the court" by locally turning off the camera.

A number of courses requiring demonstrations have been found to be more effectively taught through the use of television at the University of Colorado School of Nursing. In the courses on anatomy and physiology, for example, the complexity of laboratory equipment required to perform certain experiments made it impractical for each nurse to go through the procedure individually with an instructor. Each student nurse now benefits by seeing enlarged closeups of the experiment, together with hearing a running commentary. Fig. 6-8 shows a typical experiment which involves the study of a turtle heart for fibrillation, chemical and electrical heart block, and responses to chemical and electrical stimuli.

Courtesy Sylvania Electric Products, Inc.

Fig. 6-6. Overflow audience at commencement exercises at Batavia, New York, viewing proceedings via closed-circuit television.

TV is being used to instruct student teachers in ITV techniques at the College of St. Francis, Joliet, Illinois. In their introductory courses on broadcasting, which cover both radio and television, they are taught the production of a televised lesson, techniques of presentation, and the versatile uses of television in teaching.

South Carolina was one of the first states to recognize the value of closed-circuit television and ETV as a teaching tool. Experiments began with the medium in South Carolina in 1958. The results have been so rewarding that the use of television as an educational tool was extended to all 46 counties (Fig. 6-9) in time for the 1962-1963 school year. Courses now being taught via television include algebra, geometry, physical science, the history

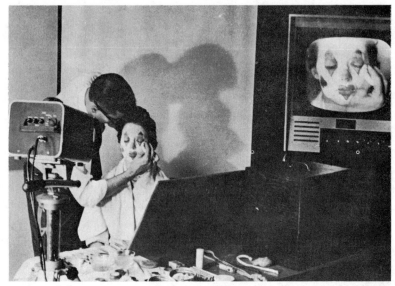

Courtesy Sylvania Electric Products, Inc.

Fig. 6-7. Closed-circuit television being used in a class in theatrical makeup at Morehead State College, Kentucky.

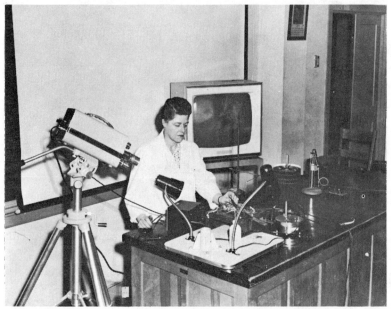

Courtesy Sylvania Electric Products, Inc.

Fig. 6-8. An experiment in anatomy being telecast to a group of nurses.

of South Carolina, and French. Lessons are video-tape recorded for distribution throughout the school TV system.

An unusual teaching application for closed-circuit television is performed daily at the Brooks Institute of Photography at Santa Barbara, California. For example, a large classroom in portraiture can observe the posing and lighting of a model and see the results in photographic form by viewing a 23-inch TV screen (Fig. 6-10).

Courtesy South Carolina Educational TV Center

Fig. 6-9. Statewide closed-circuit ETV network in South Carolina.

Without the aid of television, each student has to stand in line to peer through the ground glass of the portrait camera itself. A closeup lens enables the students in the retouching class to watch the manual dexterity of the instructor.

Pilot Landing Aid Television (PLAT), developed by the U.S. Navy and Ampex, is a completely integrated system of electronic picture and sound recording. It is designed to monitor and record aircraft landing operations aboard an aircraft carrier, from approach through final recovery, under day and night conditions. The recordings are played back for post-flight analysis and evaluation. Four closed-circuit television cameras are used. Two are at the centerline and are stabilized to the optical landing system of

Courtesy Sylvania Electric Products, Inc.

Fig. 6-10. TV camera and monitor being used to replace ground-glass camera in portraiture class at Brooks Institute of Photography, Santa Barbara, California.

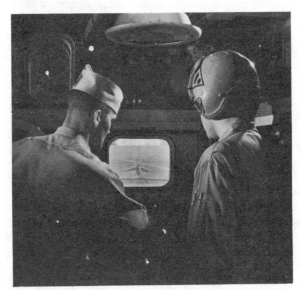

Courtesy Ampex Corp.

Fig. 6-11. The monitor in a PLAT installation on an aircraft carrier.

the aircraft carrier to pick up and follow the aircraft. The aircraft attitude and glide slopes are displayed on picture monitors in combination with the signals from a third special-effects camera focused on a data board carrying time, date, wind velocity, and aircraft landing speed. After touchdown and during recovery, the aircraft is monitored by the fourth camera on the island

Courtesy Radio Corporation of America

Fig. 6-12. A line telecast at University of Akron, Ohio.

structure of the ship as the airplane passes over the centerline cameras. The entire operation is recorded on video tape as it is being monitored. Prior to this system, the technique was to use a standard 16-mm motion-picture camera setup. This did not permit visual monitoring throughout the ship, and the processing of film took a minimum of six hours, which reduced the value of the recordings in debriefing and instruction sessions. With closed-circuit television and video tape recordings in PLAT, pilots (Fig. 6-11) can see the action and evaluate it for self-improvement minutes later.

Courtesy Radio Corporation of America

Fig. 6-13. Classroom at University of Akron, Ohio.

Divinity students at Columbia Theological Seminary, Decatur, Georgia, evaluate and improve their speaking effectiveness through the use of closed-circuit television and video tape recording. At the College of William and Mary, Williamsburg,

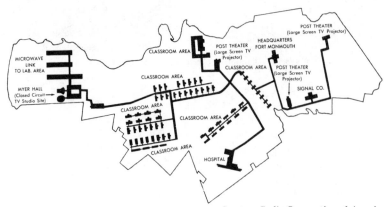

Courtesy Radio Corporation of America

Fig. 6-14. Closed-circuit ETV system at Fort Monmouth, New Jersey.

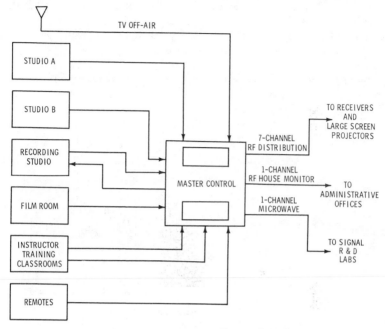

Fig. 6-15. Block diagram showing feeds to and from master control room at Fort Monmouth, New Jersey.

Virginia, the complete beginner's course in Spanish has been recorded on video tape. Thus, the instructors are released for special work with individual students.

The British Broadcasting Corporation operates the oldest educational television service in the world. It was inaugurated in May, 1952, when 20 experimental programs were transmitted

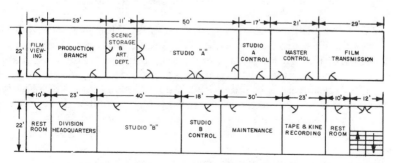

Fig. 6-16. Floor plan of the Fort Monmouth ETV system.

via closed circuit to six secondary schools in London. In 1957 the service was instituted on a regular basis with a schedule of four programs a week for 350 schools. By 1963, 13 programs were being transmitted every week. Approximately 4,000 schools are equipped to receive them.

Eleven central Texas colleges share the curriculum of courses by means of video tape and closed-circuit microwave links. Specially qualified teachers whose courses are unique in content

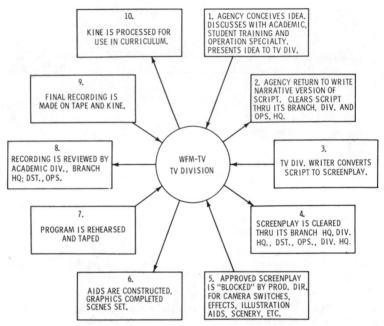

Courtesy Radio Corporation of America

Fig. 6-17. Steps in the evolution of a typical educational TV program at Fort Monmouth.

were selected for the Texas Educational Microwave Project (TEMP). The program permits the presentation of traditional courses from a central point, thus freeing a large number of classroom instructors from lecturing to several sections, giving them time for research and individual student guidance. All TEMP courses are on video tape. There are no system-wide exams. Each classroom instructor examines and grades his students.

More than six miles of coaxial cable, microphone lines, and miscellaneous other wiring thread throughout the campus of the University of Akron, which makes closed-circuit television an important part of its schedule of instruction. A large number of classrooms are connected by intercom to the broadcast studio. This novel arrangement enables students and classroom instructors to query the TV instructor. A typical studio scene is shown in Fig. 6-12 and a classroom in Fig. 6-13.

An extensive facility is operated by the U.S. Army Signal Corps at Fort Monmouth, New Jersey. It started in 1951 with a single camera and monitor on an experimental basis. As can be seen in Fig. 6-14, the present installation is quite comprehensive,

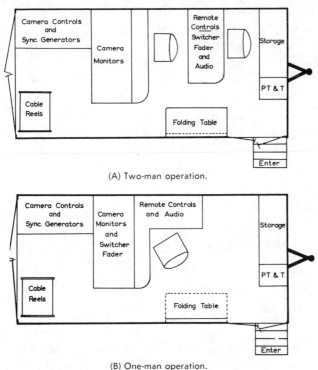

(A) Two-man operation.

(B) One-man operation.

Courtesy Spencer-Kennedy Laboratories, Inc.

Fig. 6-18. Floor plans of trailers used at San Jose State College, California.

covering the main points of student assembly and instruction. A diagram of the facilities that feed the master control room is given in Fig. 6-15. The diagram in Fig. 6-16 is of special interest to those preparing floor plans for their own operations. It shows the arrangement of the studios, control rooms, and special services. The sequence of events relative to preparation of a telecast are shown in Fig. 6-17. WFM-TV are the call letters used internally at Fort Monmouth as a simple identification. Approximately

10,000 students each year receive some part of their training through the closed-circuit television system.

San Jose State College in California has had several important years of experience with ETV and ITV. The California State Department of Education, Division of State Colleges and Teacher Education, through a committee on curriculum study, has given general direction and coordination at San Jose and at other colleges in the State College System. Television pickup and

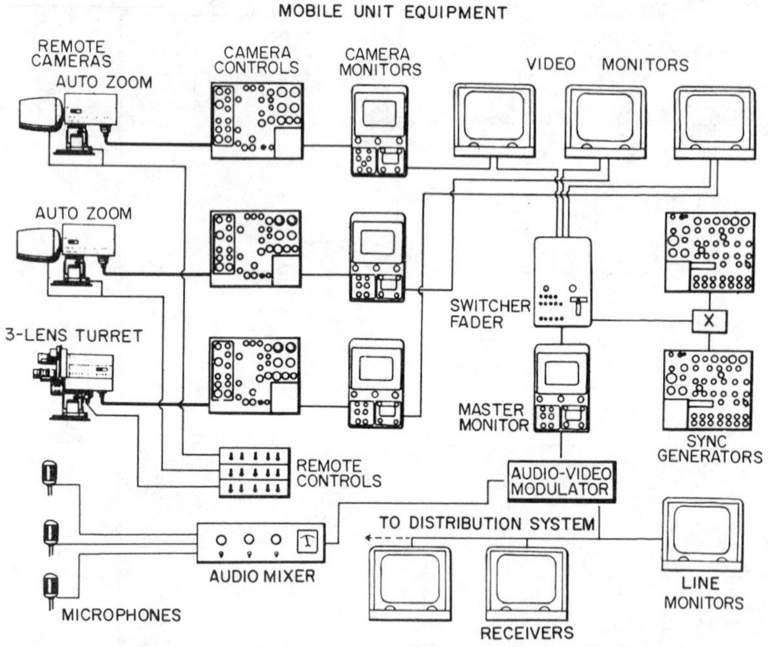

MOBILE UNIT EQUIPMENT

Courtesy Spencer-Kennedy Laboratories, Inc.

Fig. 6-19. Block diagram of TV equipment at San Jose State College.

transmission from four public schools to San Jose State College are a major activity in the ITV project. A war surplus trailer was reconditioned by the college, and television system components were installed to enable transportation of equipment from school to school. The first trailer, Fig. 6-18A, was designed for two-man operation. However, the equipment was later rearranged (Fig. 6-18B) to make one-man operation possible. In effect, the school system was provided with a mobile unit patterned after those used by commercial-TV broadcast stations. However, unlike commercial TV stations, the trailer is equipped with remote controls for the cameras. This makes possible complete one-man operation of a pickup and transmission from a remote location. Fig. 6-19 details the equipment carried in the mobile van. Remote control is provided for lens zoom, pan, and tilt actions without requiring a cameraman at the scene of action. Fig. 6-20 shows the floor plan of the studio, control room, and peripheral service area at the college.

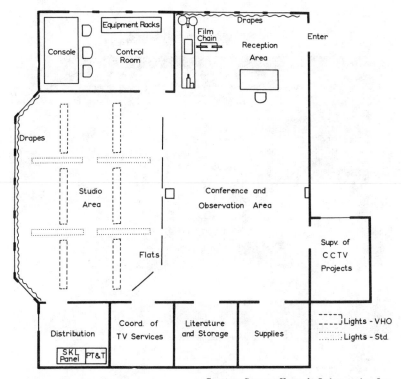

Courtesy Spencer-Kennedy Laboratories, Inc.

Fig. 6-20. Floor plan of ITV Center at San Jose State College.

At the ITV center of the University of California, Santa Barbara, the operator seated at the master control console (Fig. 6-21) is able to perform all electronic operations at the one position. The studio is at his left. The view in Fig. 6-22 is from the studio into the control room.

Fig. 6-23 is another view of the master control room. The control console is in the foreground and the equipment racks are in the background. The control console contains (from left to right): custom-made audio mixer units with vertical fade controls, script racks with slide and film projector control switches (center), and the video controls for four vidicon cameras (right). Two of the cameras are in the studio for the instructor's picture—one for the microscope, and the other for the telecine operation. The racks contain power supplies, sync generators, video switcher equipment, patch bays for audio and video feeds to the classrooms, and the control room monitors.

Courtesy Electra Megadyne, Inc.

Fig. 6-21. Master control console at ITV center at University of California, Santa Barbara.

A typical ITV-studio arrangement is shown in Fig. 6-24. The vertically mounted camera on the table is being used in microscopy. Fig. 6-25 is a closeup view of the microscope arrangement. A typical classroom scene is given in Fig. 6-26. Here two monitors are mounted from the ceiling and a third, pedestal-mounted unit is at the front of the room.

Teaching by television is most effectively done when the team approach is used rather than the concept of a single teacher for a group of students. Included among the TV-team members are the classroom teacher, the TV teacher, the producer, and the supervisor or consultant in the particular subject areas to be telecast. This primary group meets with the school officials to estab-

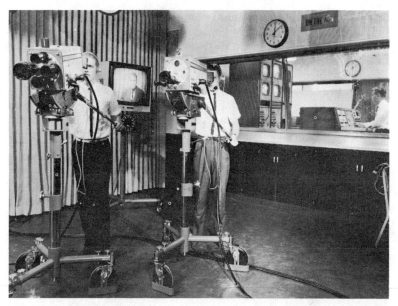

Courtesy Electra Megadyne, Inc.

Fig. 6-22. View from studio into control room at University of California, Santa Barbara.

Courtesy Electra Megadyne, Inc.

Fig. 6-23. The master control room of University of California ITV center.

lish the curriculum and techniques best suited to the needs of the individual school. Progress meetings are held regularly to evaluate the need for modifications, additions, or deletions from the schedule. At least one member of the team, often the producer, should be fully aware of the technical facilities and its capabilities. He acts as technical advisor during the meetings.

The operating or production personnel needed for closed-circuit telecasts varies with the scope and complexity of the equipment and the curriculum. If only a single camera and a monitor func-

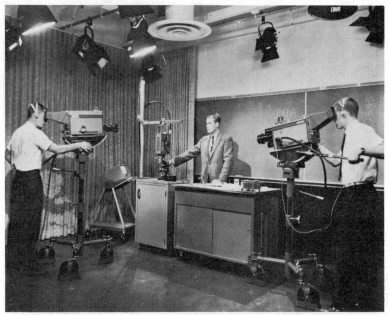

Courtesy Electra Megadyne, Inc.

Fig. 6-24. A typical ITV studio arrangement at University of California.

tioning as an enlarger are used in a classroom, the instructor himself comprises the entire staff. He can become completely familiar, after brief instruction, with setting up and operating the camera and monitor. On the other hand, a complex system may require a full-time paid operator or group of operating personnel. Usually, student operators and paid technical specialists are both used. The latter perform the maintenance, service, and master-control operations. The most frequently used titles and their associated functions are:

Producer-Director—The producer-director combines proficiency in education with a broad knowledge of TV techniques and operation. He is responsible for the end product that appears on the screen and is heard through the sound channel.

Cameramen—Only a minimum of training is needed to handle today's uncomplicated vidicon cameras; high school and college students have proven themselves to be quite competent. The cameramen take "orders" for camera positions and angles from the producer-director while the program is being televised.

Technicians—Specific training which may have been acquired formally or by actual working background is required of the technicians. They operate the video and audio mixing controls, switchers, faders, intercom, and related apparatus.

Maintenance Engineers—The maintenance engineers are needed to keep equipment in service and to gain maximum assurance of reliability of the equipment. They may be paid technical employees on the staff, or they may be obtained on a contract basis from sources outside the school system.

Film-Chain Operators—Multiplexers and other audio-visual devices considered to be a part of the closed-circuit system are

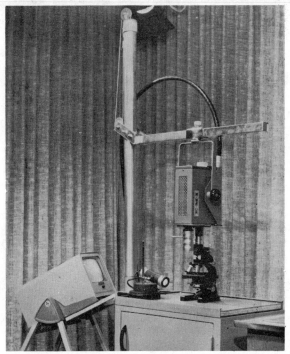

Courtesy Electra Megadyne, Inc.

Fig. 6-25. Closeup view of microscopic arrangement.

Courtesy Electra Megadyne, Inc.

Fig. 6-26. A typical classroom scene at University of California, Santa Barbara.

handled by the film-chain operators. Often this operator is assigned the responsibility for procurement, inspection, and filing of films and slides.

Graphic Arts Manager—The preparation of specific materials such as charts, slides, signs, back panels, special sets, and photography is handled by the graphic arts manager. He should have a thorough knowledge of materials, colors, and lighting to enable the team to achieve maximum use of the visual aspects of the telecast.

There are many other jobs to be performed; they fall under the self-explanatory titles of assistant director, script girl, stagehand, boom operator, lighting director, and floor manager. The personnel needs for such functions are dictated by the complexity of the program schedule and the nature of the telecasts. It is estimated that an entire crew, other than the maintenance group, can be given initial training in a minimum of five days. Of course, their skill will increase with experience. Engineering colleges frequently are able to become self-sufficient with respect to equipment maintenance and service by the very nature of the courses they teach, drawing upon faculty and students for such specialized work.

Closed-Circuit Television in Commerce and Industry

T HE DEMAND FOR IMPROVED and more efficient techniques in business communications has been increasing at an extremely rapid rate. Closed-circuit television plays an important part in the transmission, reception, and visual readout of data, documents, signatures, alphanumerics, and the many forms of general intercommunications essential to the daily conduct of a complex business world.

Commerce has always considered the verbal transmission of facts and figures to be wholly unreliable. However, commercial interests can no longer tolerate the undependability and time-consuming delays caused by physically transporting data sheets and business documents within modern office buildings and across a city. In some instances, nothing but a visual comparison between two documents can serve the conduct of business at hand. For example, a newly submitted signature must often be checked against one maintained on file. Bringing the two signatures together could create serious inconvenience and significantly delay the next step in the transaction. Closed-circuit television systems are providing important time-saving and highly reliable techniques that help to speed the flow of commerce. This medium of communications makes possible instantaneous "transportation" of any data that can be seen by the human eye—from room to room; building to building; and, with the incorporation of microwave links, from city to city.

BANKING AND FINANCE

Closed-circuit television systems are performing important functions in the operations of banks and savings and loan institutions. Growing pains brought on by limited space and increased competition demand improved customer service. Banking and finance officials are investigating new techniques for handling the overflow of paper work and the time-consuming, though essential, signature and document verifications. The diagram of a typical closed-circuit television system that provides a means for intra-bank video communications for signature verification, records

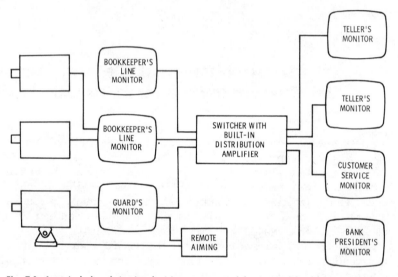

Fig. 7-1. A typical closed-circuit television system used for internal bank communications.

transmissions, and security is given in Fig. 7-1. A voice intercom or telephone system is used simultaneously with the picture transmission.

A television system provides a communications link between the dual headquarters of the First National City Bank of New York. More than four miles separate the offices in the downtown financial district and the uptown offices in the midst of the commercial center. Daily meetings are opened with a view on the television monitor of the money position of the bank. After discussion, the cameras and monitors are switched to provide two-way video and voice communications between the two offices. Both locations are equipped with 27-inch monitors. One camera is mounted for viewing the conferees; a second one transmits closeups of documents or any other desired information. Questions, answers, and business of the day can be handled just as though both groups were in the same room, without the inconvenience of requiring either group to travel to the other's location.

One of the largest closed-circuit television installations for bank security is installed at the Harris Trust and Savings Bank in Chicago. Twelve cameras provide constant surveillance of person-

Courtesy Dage-Bell Div., Raytheon Co.

Fig. 7-2. Monitors for closed-circuit television system at Harris Trust and Savings Bank of Chicago.

nel and customer activities in each of the six departments located on four floors. The nerve center of this installation is pictured in Fig. 7-2. In this ground floor location a unique eight-monitor panel provides the guard with a constant view of all operations. One of the cameras is shown at the upper right of Fig. 7-3. Here the delivery of $65,000 by Brink's guards is under the surveillance of the camera.

The first monitor (Fig. 7-2) displays the pictures from the second-floor Loan and Discount Department. The fourth-floor Securities Accounting Department is seen on the second monitor. The third and fourth monitors receive pictures from the basement Coupon and the sixth-floor Trust Departments. Each of the de-

Courtesy Dage-Bell Div., Raytheon Co.

Fig. 7-3. Camera in currency department of Harris Trust and Savings Bank of Chicago.

partments has at least two scanning TV cameras which take pictures from different angles and relay them to their respective monitors. If something irregular is observed on any of the first four monitors, the picture can be transferred to a fifth or sixth monitor and held for prolonged observation. Monitors seven and eight show the activities of the basement Currency and the sixth-floor Stock Transfer Departments. The camera for the latter department is equipped with a wide-angle lens to enable coverage of the 70-foot depth of this department. The objective of the closed-circuit television system is to maintain maximum security with a minimum staff of guards.

A bank can provide fast and accurate service to its drive-in customers with a closed-circuit television system. The customer drives up to the "island" unit pictured in Fig. 7-4. The outside unit has a small door which is teller-controlled and into which the customer inserts his passbook and other papers essential to the transaction. The papers are carried to and from the inside teller station through a pneumatic tube. Both inside and outside locations are equipped with a camera, monitor, and a voice intercom system enabling the customer and teller to converse "face to face." Fig. 7-5 shows the teller station. The TV camera is directly below the monitor, and the pneumatic tubes and controls are at the center. The left panel is for future expansion of the system.

Courtesy Sylvania Electric Products, Inc.

Fig. 7-4. An island unit of a TV drive-in bank.

Some bank installations include a signature verification camera and monitor, with the camera installed in the file room, usually a basement location, and the monitor at the teller's cage. This latter system is usually completely independent of the drive-in system. At the request of a teller, an associate at the files places the original signature card on the table designed to hold the closeup camera. The teller then sees an enlargement of the signature at his monitor and is able to make rapid and positive indentification. In order to achieve maximum definition, banking systems use video-frequency systems and, of course, closed circuit

Courtesy Sylvania Electric Products, Inc.

Fig. 7-5. The teller station of a TV drive-in bank.

Courtesy Dage-Bell Div., Raytheon Co.

Fig. 7-6. Teller at Pioneer Bank and Trust Co. of Shreveport, Louisiana.

to insure the privacy essential to the personal nature of the business at hand.

Figs. 7-6 and 7-7 show a unique system employed by the Pioneer Bank and Trust Co. of Shreveport, Louisiana. The tellers (Fig. 7-6) can communicate with the bookkeeping departments to secure customer information. On request via intercom, TV pictures of records, signature cards, ledger sheets, and statements are transmitted to the monitor at the right. The heart of the system is the unique TV scooter pictured in Fig. 7-7. This unit moves on tracks in front of the bank files, and pictures are transmitted from it to the monitors at key locations in the main and branch banks.

The unit pictured in Fig. 7-8 was designed especially for simplified transmission of documents by closed-circuit television. It contains a camera and a control unit which automatically compensates for lighting. The operator places the document to be televised face down on the glass plate and turns the switch on. The information is then transmitted to all properly connected monitors.

Courtesy Dage-Bell Div., Raytheon Co.

Fig. 7-7. "TV scooter" in Pioneer Bank and Trust Co. of Shreveport, Louisiana.

Courtesy General Precision, Inc.

Fig. 7-8. A unit designed for simplified transmission of documents via closed-circuit television.

HOTELS, MOTELS, AND APARTMENTS

Many hotels and motels make multiple use of their closed-circuit television systems. In addition to the conventional uses of television for entertainment in guest rooms, cameras are placed in the parking lots and side entrances for surveillance and security. It is claimed that motels, for example, suffer more losses through guests who walk off or drive off with motel property than they do through burglars. Motels that have installed security closed-circuit television and post notices of its existence and use have reported an immediate reduction in losses through mysterious disappearances. Of course, in surveillance of parking areas and side entrances, protection is also provided for the guests' property and physical well-being.

Cameras installed at the swimming pool and the restaurant are often connected to the master TV antenna and the distribution system so that a guest, following the instructions given on the TV set in his room, can tune to a specified channel and see the activities at those locations without leaving his room. Further uses for the TV system include internal advertising of the hotel or motel facilities or a nearby shopping center. In New York City, a closed-circuit television facility is specially programmed to subscribing

Courtesy Bell Television, Inc.

Fig. 7-9. "Watchdog" television in lobby of apartment building.

hotels, providing the guests a television guide to places to go, things to see and do, and local advertising.

An added measure of security is afforded to the tenants of an apartment building when a television "watchdog" is installed. Figs. 7-9 and 7-10 show a typical installation. It consists of a camera in the lobby and a monitor in the apartment which operates in conjunction with the usual voice interphone. Thus, the tenant can verify the voice and person of the caller before pressing the admit button of the lobby door. In some installations, cameras have been placed in elevators with monitors in the lobby for the

Courtesy Bell Television, Inc.

Fig. 7-10. Tenant unit of the "watchdog" television system.

doorman to observe and to provide security against mishaps to property and tenants.

OTHER COMMERCIAL APPLICATIONS

Applications for closed-circuit television can be found in practically any type of commercial enterprise. Closed-circuit television is being put to more and more uses each day, either to save time or as a convenience to those using the facilities.

Supermarkets and Department Stores

Aisles and checkout counters of stores can be monitored so that personnel can be shifted to assist in busy traffic areas. Systems have been used in in-store promotions and fashion shows, with cameras focused on merchandise or models, and monitors placed in windows to "pull traffic" into the store. The meat department of one busy supermarket has provided a monitor at the customer location. The butcher then displays the cut of meat via the television system for the approval of the customer.

A novel application is shown in Fig. 7-11. This installation is used by a jewelry store to promote its service facilities. The camera (upper left) is focused on the repair men at work on the floor above the store. The picture is displayed on a monitor in the store. Another monitor is seen at the top of the picture.

Parking Lots and Garages

Multiple levels of a building can be surveyed by television to guide customers to vacant spots for parking, as well as to provide security observation of parked cars.

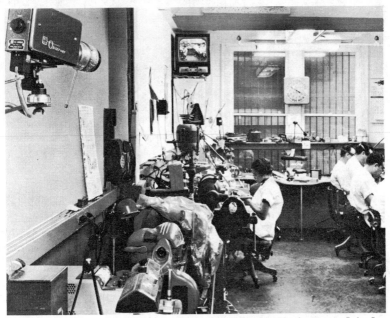

Courtesy Blonder-Tongue Labs, Inc.

Fig. 7-11. Closed-circuit television being used to promote service facilities of a jewelry store.

Nightclubs

Places of entertainment, such as supper clubs and nightclubs, have made interesting use of closed-circuit television. At New York's famous Latin Quarter, for example, television enables the manager to monitor the floor show at his office desk. In addition, a camera focused on the stage feeds pictures to the orchestra leader (Fig. 7-12), whose field of vision is restricted. With the aid of closed-circuit television, he can keep the music cues "tight" and in synchronism with the show.

Courtesy Sylvania Electric Products, Inc.

Fig. 7-12. Closed-circuit television being used to coordinate orchestra with stage.

Public Gathering Places

Public gathering places benefit from closed-circuit television systems in many ways. Overflow crowds are able to see the main attractions and other activities at remote sections of the grounds via closed-circuit systems. A large closed-circuit color television system operated during the 1964-1965 New York World's Fair. The system operated for 12 hours a day, with 5 minutes of each broadcast hour used by the Fair management for news announcements and reports of coming attractions. Approximately 250 color-TV sets were strategically located throughout the fairgrounds.

Closed-circuit TV is also used for security surveillance of public places. The Cleveland Art Museum has 33 cameras guarding some of its more rare art treasures. The guard can see an entire floor at a glance.

Large auditoriums used for sales meetings can have a negative effect on participants located at sections quite far from the speaker. Closed-circuit television can be used to eliminate the "remote" feeling. Cameras are focused on the speaker and monitors are placed throughout the auditorium.

Churches have found that closed-circuit television provides an effective way to increase their seating capacity. For example, prior to the installation of a television camera and monitors at the

Bethany Baptist Church in northwest Philadelphia, worshippers who could not be accommodated were seated in a Sunday School room where they could hear the services over a public address system but could not see the pulpit. With camera and monitors, the services are seen and heard simultaneously. A similar installation provided a solution to the overflow attendance at the Brookdale Baptist Church in Bloomfield, N. J. Many other churches have found it advantageous to lease closed-circuit systems for special occasions when a large attendance is expected.

Contractors

Life is being made more interesting, if not easier, for "sidewalk superintendents" through closed-circuit television. Cameras are located at otherwise inaccessible locations of buildings under construction to feed pictures to sidewalk monitors. "Superintendents" thus can see closeup views of the skywalking activities of the men high up in the structures. Northgate Apartments in Camden, New Jersey, installed a camera on the eighteenth floor of the building while it was being erected. A monitor in the rental office gave prospective tenants a dramatic view as it might appear from a top-floor apartment. Closed-circuit television played an important part in the new construction of the approach system for linking the lower level of the George Washington Bridge, New York, with the Cross-Bronx Expressway. A TV camera, installed atop a five-story building, scanned the entire construction site. The project manager could remote-control the camera for pan, tilt, and zoom; thus he could locate and study trouble spots. Then, by two-way radio, he directed men and equipment. A weatherproof housing allowed all-weather operation of the camera.

Advertising Agencies

Advertising agencies active in the broadcast television field make excellent use of a closed-circuit television installation within their own facilities. Several large agencies have a TV studio as part of their in-house facilities. Fig. 7-13 shows a test of a proposed television commercial in the studio of one agency. The comprehensive master-control installation of this same agency is pictured in Fig. 7-14. This type of installation is used to test commercials, audition talent, and preview live program material. Creative personnel and clients gain from the benefits offered by the simulation of the actual broadcast.

Reception Rooms

Reception rooms of professional offices can be left unattended without embarrassment or inconvenience to visitors when they

Courtesy General Precision, Inc.

Fig. 7-13. The TV studio in the N. W. Ayer Advertising Agency.

Courtesy General Precision, Inc.

Fig. 7-14. Master control installation at N. W. Ayer Advertising Agency.

are equipped with a TV camera. Monitors inside the office permit continuous viewing of the reception area so that visitors can be attended to immediately.

Auction Houses

Monitors placed throughout the seating area at auctions can bring closeup views of merchandise and other offerings to prospective bidders. Many who otherwise might not make bids are encouraged to do so. Selling time is saved and more bids are

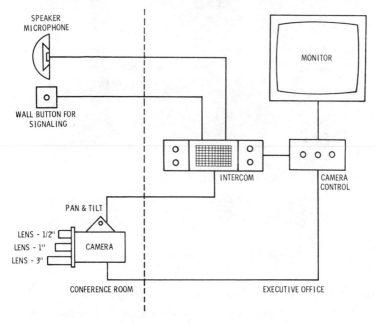

Fig. 7-15. Block diagram of a conference television installation.

received by the auctioneer by reducing inconveniences. In addition, overflow audiences can also be accommodated by the television system.

Conference Room Television

The busy executive can use television as an extension of the conference telephone and voice intercom to participate in a conference without having to leave his office. Such a system is diagrammed in Fig. 7-15. The system can also be used to view charts, data, models, and prototypes that cannot conveniently be brought to his office for examination.

Courtesy Sylvania Electric Products, Inc.

Fig. 7-16. Closed-circuit television installation at TWA, Kennedy International Airport, New York.

Airline Terminals

Flight arrival and departure information is displayed on TV monitors at airline check-in counters and waiting rooms for customer convenience and to improve the efficiency of airline personnel in answering questions regarding flight information. Fig. 7-16 shows a popular technique; a camera in the airline traffic control office is focused on a menu-type board with removable letters and numerals. Additions, corrections, and up-to-date data are quickly inserted for viewing on the monitors. Video-frequency cameras and monitors are usually employed.

Community Antenna Television

More than 1,000 communities in the United States are being served by Community Antenna Television (CATV) systems. Without CATV those communities would not be able to receive usable pictures from standard commercial-broadcast TV stations.

Frequently the point of program origin being viewed by the subscribers to the CATV system is at a great distance from the point of reception. Therefore, weather reports transmitted by the TV station are of no value to the viewers. Enterprising CATV operators have installed their own weather stations with a closed-circuit television camera focused on the weather instruments. The picture is fed to the coaxial cable and can be seen by tuning to a designated and otherwise unused TV channel on a 24-hour basis. Any subscriber to the system can then get an up-to-the-minute weather report, from which he can do his own forecasting. In one such system, referred to by its manufacturer as *Weatherscan*, a camera is mounted on a platform that moves on a track so that it scans a linear arrangement of 9-inch-diameter weather instruments and panels. Local announcements of public service or commercial information are placed on the panels. The instruments are connected to continuously operating sensors mounted above the CATV building.

Ticker-Tape TV

Fast decisions demand the best, most complete, and most automatic communications techniques. Several brokerage firms have used closed-circuit television equipment to provide the means. Stock exchange tapes can be viewed by TV cameras as in Fig. 7-17, and the information fed continuously to desks throughout the office, or even to branch offices (Fig. 7-18). This reduces the costs of brokerage operation by eliminating the need for a multitude of ticker-tape units. When additional readout positions are needed, a relatively less expensive TV monitor and its connecting cable are installed. Furthermore, the distraction of the noise caused by the "ticker" is eliminated.

INDUSTRIAL APPLICATIONS

If only the number of systems in operation is considered, industrial applications for closed-circuit television are in the majority. Closed-circuit television permits significant improvements in industrial efficiency, quality control, processes, and techniques of materials handling. As a direct result of closed-circuit television, dramatic advances have been made in regard to safety of operating personnel. Closed-circuit television is used to extend the limits of normal vision and to overcome or compensate for limitations of biological factors of the human physique and its capabilities to withstand hostile environments.

With closed-circuit television as a working tool, large numbers of gauges, meters, and other indicating devices can be viewed

Fig. 7-17. Installation designed to pick up and transmit stock exchange information from ticker tapes.

Courtesy General Precision, Inc.

Courtesy General Precision, Inc.

Fig. 7-18. Ticker-tape information being displayed on a monitor in a brokerage office.

simultaneously and, if necessary, safely at a remote distance. The movement of components, raw goods, and finished merchandise can be controlled, supervised, and dispatched to and from warehouses, piers, loading docks, and platforms through the placement of cameras at elevations and angles not practicable for personnel.

Ruggedized cameras can look inside open-hearth furnaces for visual inspection, assist operators in grasping hot ingots of metals, and provide "eyes" for mechanical robots in the handling of explosive or radioactive materials. Closed-circuit television cameras can enter quarters too small for the human body, and places too hot or too cold to permit survival. They provide a means for giving extra "eyes" to machine operators, and enlarged views of minute parts for improved inspection or assembly.

The Permanente Cement Company of Hawaii has three separate systems in use. Cement raw materials (coral, clinker, basalt, and gypsum and silica sand) are stored in six silos and two star bins. Materials are fed to the mills by continuously proportioning and weighing feeders. Feed proportions are controlled by the chemists in the laboratory, and the overall feed rate may be controlled by the chemists or the mill operator. Two cameras are mounted over the belt conveyor under the storage silos. Fig. 7-19 is a block diagram of this system. Information supplied by the television system helps both the chemists and the miller in maintaining a vigil over the feed belts. Each of the cameras is installed in a dust-free housing. Both chemist and mill operator see the same information at the same time.

The kiln areas of the Permanente Cement Company have the most extensive system of the three closed-circuit television installations. (See Fig. 7-20.) A camera is installed in a weatherproof housing with a heavy-duty pan-and-tilt support. It is mounted atop a slurry basin, in a position that commands a view of the massive rotating kiln. A second camera is mounted to view a huge chain and sprocket drive, to detect any malfunction which could interrupt the constant flow of clinker away from the kiln. The third camera views the clinker as it is transferred from a vibrating conveyor to an elevator. The operator in Fig. 7-21 can instantly determine protective measures, if the clinker should overflow because of a jammed receiving hopper. A separate monitor is used with each camera; thus, the entire system can be monitored simultaneously by one man.

The simplest system of the Permanente installation uses one camera and one monitor (Fig. 7-22). Raw materials are discharged into a hopper above the primary jaw crusher. A vibrating grizzly feeder bypasses material under six inches to the crusher discharge conveyor and feeds oversize material to a jaw crusher. The discharged products are carried by a 24-inch conveyor belt to the secondary crushing station. The camera is installed above the jaw crusher and grizzly feeder to enable the visual detection of any stoppage caused by jamming. By watching the monitor, the operator of the equipment controls the rate of material flow from the primary grizzly feeder.

The Dragon Cement Company at its Northampton, Pennsylvania, plant has used television to improve the control and handling of heavy bulk materials. The operator, watching a series of

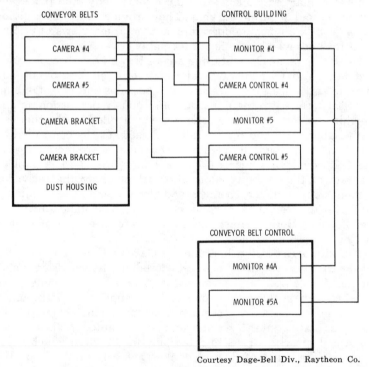

Courtesy Dage-Bell Div., Raytheon Co.

Fig. 7-19. Block diagram of conveyor-belt monitoring system.

monitor screens, has closeup views of the operations of dumping limestone from trucks into the receiving hoppers and the loading of skip cars from the hoppers.

The American Smelting and Refining Company, at its Silver Bell Unit near Tucson, Arizona, uses closed-circuit television to maintain its huge daily output. Four TV cameras are mounted in environmental housings in remote areas of the crusher building. Summer temperatures in the shade at Silver Bell may hover at 115° F. The primary crusher is being observed by an environmental-housed TV camera at middle right in Fig. 7-23. The equipment is crushing pieces of ore, and the camera provides warnings against possible jams that might stall the giant motor. The primary crusher receives a load from 75-ton semitrailer trucks every 10 minutes. It feeds a stockpile outside the crusher area, and conveyor belts reclaim from the stockpile to feed the secondary

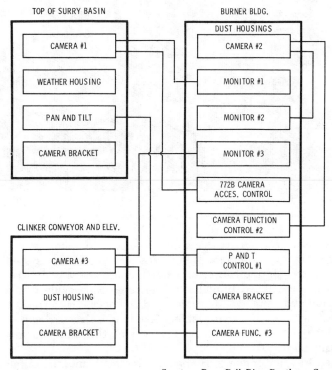

Courtesy Dage-Bell Div., Raytheon Co.

Fig. 7-20. Block diagram of kiln-area television system.

crushers inside the building. Two environmental-housed cameras are used to observe the conveyors. The control console (Fig. 7-24) incorporates video monitors, a video switcher, and dual camera control units. It is located on a platform subjected to the vibration of the secondary crushers. Note the dust mask being worn by the control operator; this is one of the reasons for the environmental housings for the cameras.

A lead and zinc mine in the state of Washington uses closed-circuit television to improve the efficiency of hoist operations. From a distance of 1,500 feet, the operator, using a camera and

Courtesy Dage-Bell Div., Raytheon Co.

Fig. 7-21. Monitor panel in Permanente Cement Co. installation.

monitor, controls an ore car which dumps into a storage pit some 450 feet away from him. Before installation of the system, his only control or indication of trouble had been by line of sight through a darkened tunnel and markings on a cable drum. The electronic viewing capability enabled the operator to speed up his control without impairing safety, so that extra carloads of ore could be pulled from the lower level of the mine during each working shift.

The Drever Company, Bethayres, Pennsylvania, manufactured a 400-foot roller hearth furnace now in operation in Houston,

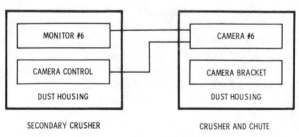

Courtesy Dage-Bell Div., Raytheon Co.

Fig. 7-22. Block diagram of secondary-crusher and crusher-and-chute television system.

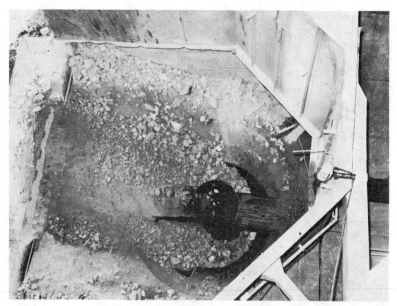

Courtesy Cohu/KinTel Electronics

Fig. 7-23. Primary-crusher installation at American Smelting and Refining Co.

Courtesy Cohu/KinTel Electronics

Fig. 7-24. Control console at American Smelting and Refining Co.

Texas, which uses industrial television to improve operator efficiency and safety. The operator is located at a "pulpit" at the midway point of the furnace, where he monitors three critical areas of the furnace.

Cameras are located at each smelter of the National Lead Company plant at Perth Amboy, New Jersey. Monitors in the superintendent's office enable him to observe lead flow, potential hazards, and trouble spots. It is estimated that the television system was responsible for a 45% reduction in industrial accidents.

Courtesy Dage-Bell Div., Raytheon Co.

Fig. 7-25. Camera scanning strip of steel before it enters annealing furnace.

The camera in Fig. 7-25 is mounted on a balcony high above the galvanizing mill floor of the Midwest Steel Division, Portage, Indiana, plant of the National Steel Corporation. A TV camera scans a cleaned strip of steel just before it enters the annealing furnace. The monitor is located near the main control desk and makes it possible for the control operator to determine whether the strip is perfectly aligned to avoid kinking that could result in the breaking of the strip while in the furnace.

The camera in Fig. 7-26 is strategically located in the looping pit below the galvanizing mill floor of Midwest Steel. This camera is used to keep an around-the-clock eye on the entry and exit points of the 400-foot double-length horizontal loop storage pit. This loop serves as a reserve of cleaned steel strip prior to its entry into the galvanizing furnace. The primary purpose of the system is to monitor tracking alignment and thereby prevent kinking or breaking of the strip.

Walter G. Anderson and Associates, a printing plant located in Minneapolis, Minnesota, has used an extensive closed-circuit television installation to provide instantaneous coverage of five different production departments in its four-story building. The heart of the system is a master control console in the production conference room where five monitors, each with its own remote-control switches for its associated camera, are installed. Four cameras are permanently installed. A fifth camera is portable for use anywhere in the plant. A 30-foot monorail on which one of the remotely controlled cameras is mounted provides coverage of an L-shaped lithograph and bindery department. The remote

Courtesy Dage-Bell Div., Raytheon Co.

Fig. 7-26. Camera installed in looping pit at Midwest Steel, Portage, Indiana.

Courtesy Blonder-Tongue Labs, Inc.

Fig. 7-27. Camera observing pulp washer discharge at Brunswick Pulp and Paper Co.

controls for the camera include pan, tilt, and zoom, all while the camera rides along its rail. In addition to monitoring production and potential trouble spots, the television installation permits plant "tours" for clients without their physically leaving the conference room.

The Brunswick Paper and Pulp Company uses television to view the pulpwasher discharge and to check the flow from a belt conveyor to a distributing conveyor chute (Fig. 7-27). Clogging at any point in the system could represent the loss of thousands of dollars. With closed-circuit television, a single operator observes the process and makes adjustments in flow and composition when necessary.

Ketchikan Pulp Company, Ward Cove, Alaska, has installed a TV camera and a video monitor to watch the level of chips in its surge bins, to prevent overflow. Chips for the manufacture of pulp are sorted by screening, and the better grades are transported to surge bins that hold 400 tons of selected chips. Prior to the installation of closed-circuit television, it was necessary to have a man stationed close to the bins to safeguard constantly against the possibility of overflow. With television, the control operator, who is 1,500 feet away, can observe the level of chips for himself.

The Union Carbide Chemical Company, South Charleston, West Virginia, uses a two-camera chain to enable an operator in the control room to watch other operators in certain processing areas that are subject to physical hazard. The men in the processing areas take samples of materials from pumps and tanks within the structure. One camera is at ground level, the other at a 60-foot level. Both cameras are in vapor-proof housings. The Union Carbide Company's plant at Bound Brook, New Jersey, uses closed-circuit television to monitor the far side of a machine used in the production of plastics. Where two operators were formerly required, one is now sufficient. He can directly view his side and, through the TV monitor, can also see and control the opposite side of the machine.

The Douglas Aircraft Company, at its El Segundo Division, has used television to keep a close watch on critical operations of its huge riveting machine used to install stringers on wing panels. One operator (Fig. 7-28), with a television camera and monitor to guide him, can accurately and conveniently control start-and-stop operations by push button to prevent machine damage, wasted stock, and incorrect riveting. The camera is positioned under the wing, and the monitor provides an enlarged view of the rivets.

Courtesy Blonder-Tongue Labs, Inc.

Fig. 7-28. Closed-circuit television being used in riveting stringers to an aircraft wing.

TV carries up-to-the-minute data throughout the El Segundo, California, factory of Hughes Aircraft Company. Cameras are located in the parts department (Fig. 7-29), the machine loading scheduling department (Fig. 7-30), and the finished goods department. Information originating from or needed in each of the departments and essential to the up-time of the production and assembly lines is transmitted and received through the closed-

Courtesy Cohu/KinTel Electronics

Fig. 7-29. Parts department at Hughes Aircraft Co.

circuit television system. The up-to-the minute data make possible rapid evaluations of production flow, parts requirements, and delivery schedules. It has been estimated that the system reduced paperwork costs alone by approximately $50,000 in the first 16 months of operation.

Fig. 7-31 shows a supervisor at an assembly line checking the schedule on his monitor. The data being transmitted from any of the three departments can be selected by depressing the correct push button. Similar monitors are located in the works manager's office, purchasing, receiving, production office, and several other locations.

Fig. 7-32 shows another unusual capability of television to serve as an industrial tool. Here the action of an inside-out welding operation being performed on a solid-fuel missile chamber at the

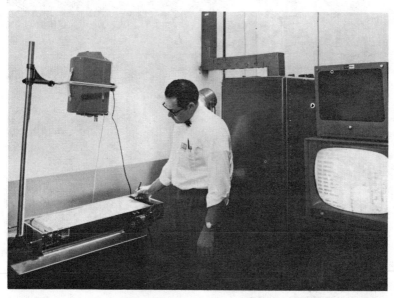

Courtesy Cohu/KinTel Electronics

Fig. 7-30. Scheduling office at Hughes Aircraft Co.

Courtesy Cohu/KinTel Electronics

Fig. 7-31. Assembly line monitor at Hughes Aircraft Co.

Courtesy Cohu/KinTel Electronics

Fig. 7-32. Closed-circuit television being used in welding of solid-fuel missile chamber.

Avco Corporation's Lycoming Division, Stratford, Connecticut, is being monitored on the screen. The teleview of the welding head and track is better than visual inspection because a four-times magnification is accomplished and a special red camera lens eliminates glare from the welding operation. Television observes highly sensitive burst tests which determine the correct heat treatment for the rocket chambers, while engineers monitor the results from a safe location.

General Dynamics Astronautics uses a closed-circuit television system in its "clean room" operations. Certain hydraulic parts intended for use in the Atlas ICBM boosters are flushed with a solvent. The solvent is then poured through a membrane filter which is examined by microscope to determine the number, size, and type of contaminants. To reduce operator fatigue and to maintain peak efficiency of the inspector, particle counting is done with the aid of a TV camera focused through the microscope and fed to a 17-inch monitor, as shown in Fig. 7-33.

Fig. 7-34 shows a microtransistor automatic assembly unit equipped with a TV camera and monitor to provide an enlarged view of the delicate operations. With the enlargement of the assembly, the operator of the equipment is better able to weld the 0.0001-inch gold wires to a 0.002-inch transistor element.

Courtesy Cohu/KinTel Electronics

Fig. 7-33. Closed-circuit television installation in "clean room" at General Dynamics Astronautics.

Courtesy Miratel Electronics, Inc.

Fig. 7-34. Microtransistor automatic assembly unit employing closed-circuit television.

SECURITY AND SURVEILLANCE

Most industrial plants have multiple entrances as a matter of convenience or necessity. The larger the plant area is, the more numerous these entrances, and the greater the distances between them. The use of electrically controlled gates makes possible the operation of a number of accesses by remote control from a single location and by a single security officer. However, surveillance of those trying to leave or enter the premises cannot normally be accomplished without posting a security officer at each access

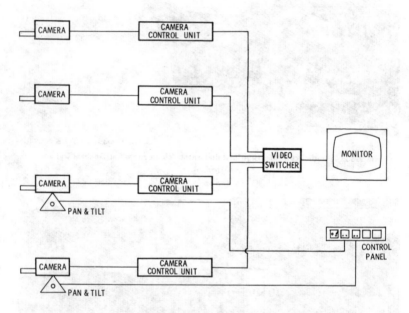

Fig. 7-35. Block diagram of a surveillance installation.

point. The need for effective visual surveillance of widespread, multiple entry and exit points is often fulfilled with closed-circuit television systems.

The block diagram of a closed-circuit television system for visual observation of multiple areas is given in Fig. 7-35. Through the use of a video switcher, a single monitor is used to selectively view the pictures fed from the cameras. In some installations it is desirable to simultaneously and continuously view the telecasts from all four cameras; in such instances the video switcher is eliminated and the camera control units are connected to individual monitors.

A typical gate installation for security is pictured in Fig. 7-36. The TV camera is installed in a weather-resistant housing and mounted on a pan-and-tilt mechanism atop the gate post. Floodlights enable nighttime operation. A speaker in a weatherproof housing enables the security officer to give instructions to those entering or leaving. The gates of this installation are operated by the security officer using remote control.

From his central location, the guard in Fig. 7-37 can observe each electrically controlled gate, an area, a border, or a fence line by television. In some installations the security officer is provided with a single monitor which is either manually or automatically switched to sequentially display the pictures being fed by each of the cameras in the system. It is more usual to provide a separate monitor for each operating camera so that surveillance of all points can be continuous and simultaneous.

Surveillance of gates and their approaches is best accomplished with a wide-angle, short-focal-length lens on the camera. The guard is made most effective when the camera is fitted with remote controls for pan, tilt, and zoom, so that he can make the most thorough checks of all areas.

Courtesy Dage-Bell Div., Raytheon Co.

Fig. 7-36. A typical gate security installation.

Courtesy Packard-Bell Electronics, Inc.

Fig. 7-37. A security officer checking arrival and departure of vehicles via closed-circuit television.

Roving guards at large plants are generally required to patrol a considerable distance on each round, punching in at several different control points. The distance varies, of course, with the size and nature of the plant, but a total of three miles or more per round is not uncommon. The route will usually take the guards indoors and outdoors, through all kinds of weather, and to areas which may be removed from telephone or alarm systems. A guard usually is not able to spend more than a few minutes at any given location. Therefore, each location is virtually unguarded for the major part of the tour period.

Experienced criminals can quickly determine the "safe" time intervals for break-in and entry when the only protection given to a property from a visual surveillance standpoint is that provided by the ambulant security officer. The physical exertion of continuing the patrol throughout a shift can tire the guard and seriously reduce his alertness and effectiveness toward the end of the shift. Inclement weather also takes its toll in effectiveness of the guard. All of these facts emphasize the extraordinary values of weather-resistant remote-controlled closed-circuit television cameras positioned at strategic points and feeding pictures to a centrally located security office where a guard views the monitors with the alarm actuating system close at hand.

Courtesy Sylvania Electric Products, Inc.

Fig. 7-38. Control center of security system at Chain Belt Co., Milwaukee, Wisconsin.

At the Bobbie Brooks Cleveland Warehouse, closed-circuit television has played an important role in security. Doorways and shipping and receiving docks are monitored by as many as 7 cameras, each with its own monitor at a central security office. A wholesale produce company uses closed-circuit television to survey the front and rear sidings, providing protection against vandalism and theft. The cameras are mounted in all-weather housings. Monitors are located in the office.

At the Olin Mathieson, East Alton, Illinois, plant, cameras and monitors provide a security check on all employees entering or leaving. One camera focuses on the entrance to give a full-length view of the area. Another camera is used to check employees' badges which are held up against a plate glass window behind which is a closed-circuit camera with closeup lens. The guard,

Courtesy Sylvania Electric Products, Inc.

Fig. 7-39. Turnstiles at entrance of Chain Belt Co.

viewing two monitors, can see the face of the badge holder and the photograph on the badge for positive identification.

The Chain Belt Company of Milwaukee, Wisconsin, automated its entrance-exit system with turnstiles and closed-circuit television. The plant facilities covered 980,000 square feet of buildings on 66 acres. Guards at each of three stations were required to check over 2,000 employee passes. Closed-circuit television enables one guard in the central security office (Fig. 7-38) to observe the three locations. One of the entrances is shown in Fig. 7-39. Employees are issued coded identification cards which are inserted in a slot at the full-height turnstiles. This releases the latch and permits the employee to enter. The control panel at the right in Fig. 7-38, however, permits the guard to override the automatic function to prevent someone from entering. One of the cameras is shown above the turnstile at the rear in Fig. 7-39.

Closed-Circuit Television in Research, Medicine, and Military and Public Service

M ORE AND MORE NEW applications are being found for closed-circuit television each day. The two preceding chapters were devoted to uses in the fields of education, commerce, and industry. These uses are more familiar to most people, but closed-circuit television is not limited to these fields. In this chapter many other applications will be considered.

RESEARCH

Research activities are increasing rapidly in all sciences. Man has become more aware than ever before of the need for more specific knowledge of himself and the universe he inhabits. His curiosity has become a hunger for facts that will enable him to understand the heretofore "nonunderstandable." Conjecture must be replaced by data which can only be acquired through the exploration of matter. Each new discovery intended to satisfy the scientist's hunger for knowledge introduces new plateaus of unknowns for which a new hunger is immediately awakened. As scientists have expressed it, "Each day we learn more and more and know less and less." New discoveries have disproven old theories and "laws." Techniques and practices based on early accepted theories have had to be discarded to make room for completely new approaches and new sets of "tools" for the scientists' world.

New instruments for research are constantly being developed. These, in turn, bring new techniques which can result in newer discoveries. To put these "discoveries" to work requires improvements, modifications, or inventions of tools and techniques. Thus, the entire process becomes regenerative.

For years closed-circuit television systems have played a quietly important role in the pursuit of scientific advancement. Although much of the work and the results are considered proprietary information or are classified company or military "secret," it is possible to describe some of the work being accomplished.

Tests and operations that accompany explorations in the nuclear sciences create a danger area of contamination that could be fatal to all forms of animal life. Yet, if science is to be served, the tests must be performed and visually observed. In work with linear accelerators, for example, provision must be made for close observation of the reactions of materials under bombardment while the instrumentation techniques in conjunction with the operation of the complex and cumbersome accelerator apparatus are studied. Obviously this is an ideal application for a closed-circuit television system. Because high resolution is requisite, only a high-quality video system can prove adequate to the task. The camera is usually fitted with a telephoto lens made with glass optics that will resist the "browning" effects of the contaminated atmosphere. Coaxial cables interconnect the camera and monitors, the latter being located at a safe distance, usually at the control desk of the linear accelerator. A second camera is focused on the instrument panel in the accelerator room and feeds pictures to an additional monitor. The scientists work in complete safety and are provided with an enlarged closeup view of the materials being exposed to the nuclear bombardment.

If it is necessary to manipulate a highly volatile material, a thick protective barrier is placed between the operator and the hazard. A mechanical robot, completely controllable so that it can be made to perform all digital motions of a mechanical simulated hand, does the actual physical contacting of the volatile substance. In absolute safety, the operator of the robot and other personnel associated with the activity observe the actions through a remotely controlled TV camera and local TV monitors. When combined with a kinescope, video tape recorder, or any other technique for making a permanent record, the action can be used for future reference or for the training of other personnel in the unusual skills involved. Of course these records can also be used for the development of new and improved techniques of handling volatile substances. The same holds true when the atmosphere is too hazardous—whether through radiation, heat or cold, noise or vibration, shock or acceleration—for animal life to survive. Closed-circuit television becomes the "eyes" for the observer; fortunately, should a mishap occur, the only loss among the personnel is the loss of the "eyes," the TV camera.

Giant rockets, smaller jet engines, and power plants whose exhausts must be observed during static tests or dynamic flights can be visually examined during those active periods through the use of closed-circuit equipment. Ruggedized cameras in environmental housings designed to withstand heat, cold, shock, noise, vibration, and other severe conditions make it possible for scientists and engineers to gain incredibly close looks at or into jet nozzles, examining parts for fatigue, observing every minute area, and hoping to witness the cause and effect as they occur.

The closed-circuit television system in Fig. 8-1 in an integral part of the Data Storage and Study Laboratory at the Aeronautic Division of the Ford Company's El Toro testing facility. The camera is mounted on a remotely controlled pan-tilt mechanism and is fitted with a zoom lens for long and closeup views. The camera is installed in a protective cell in one of the three test sites. Scientists (at a safe distance) are able to view test performances on high-resolution monitors. A closeup view of the main control console is given in Fig. 8-2. Remote controls for the camera are located above the monitor. Simultaneously with the video observation, test data are collected during a run and recorded on a Visicorder oscillograph as well as on other types of analog and digital instruments.

Firms engaged in the research, development, and test of both liquid- and solid-propellant rocket engines and advanced jet units have applied television cameras to monitoring the events at distances as close as 18 inches to the thrust nozzles during test firings. Cameras and monitors are part of the operational equipment of all Titan missile facilities. Cameras are part of the research equipment carried aboard the X-15 aircraft, enabling the transmission to ground stations of actual pictures of the pilot's reactions to the unusual flight patterns and extraordinary maneuvers of the craft. More than a few pilots have been saved by techniques of canopy and seat ejection while flying distressed military planes. The techniques and equipment were developed with the use of closed-circuit television systems providing a means for putting engineers and scientists "in the seat" of the development models.

Esso Research at Boway, New Jersey, uses CCTV to protect researchers working with prototypes for processing equipment

Courtesy Cohu/KinTel Electronics

Fig. 8-1. Data storage and study laboratory at the Aeronautic Division of the Ford Company's El Toro testing facility.

Courtesy Cohu/KinTel Electronics

Fig. 8-2. A closeup of the main control console at the Ford Company, El Toro facility.

to be used in new research. Four cameras continuously monitor the enclosed work area to observe the men at work. At the slightest indication of physical distress, as seen on the monitors, a rescue is instantly ordered.

Project Celescope, a planned orbiting astronomical observatory, is equipped with a novel vidicon picture pickup tube featuring high sensitivity and long storage time. It is expected that this tube, or a further development of it, will enable the dark side of the moon to be photographed. When the orbiting vehicle returns to a line-of-sight position with respect to earth, the picture that has been stored can be released on command and received by the ground stations.

Television cameras can provide unusual controls of contrast and image brightness. Add to this provision the same capabilities afforded at the monitor with respect to increasing the contrast and brightness of the received image, and the normally poor contrast of the fluoroscope acquires new character and the instrument becomes a more useful tool for scientific and medical research. Closed-circuit television systems used with X rays are enabling engineers to gain a fuller insight into stresses and strains of materials under specified conditions. This research has lead to the development of new materials, alloys, and configurations.

An environment-protected camera atop Kitt Peak National Observatory at Tucson, Arizona, is operated by remote control for aid in solar observation from within the comfort and safety of the observatory dome.

In the ground-locked studies of reactions of man to simulated space and space capsule environments, TV cameras go along for the "ride." As shown in Fig. 8-3, they feed back actual pictures of the actions of the scientists who perform the roles of astronauts, thereby eliminating the possibility of inaccurate interpretations of voice communications.

Fig. 8-4 shows the optical boresight tracking equipment used with radar apparatus for tracking and photographing the flight of experimental space vehicles. The TV camera is located in the cylindrical environmental housing at the top left of the photo.

Under-ice navigation by submarines has special significance to engineers in miltary, scientific research, and commercial activities. The U.S. Navy Electronics Laboratory at San Diego, California, is conducting detailed studies in an "arctic pool." The photograph in Fig. 8-5 shows the television camera in a stainless steel housing mounted on a stainless-steel–housed pan and tilt unit. The assembly is secured to the floor of an ice chamber that is flooded with water and ice is formed above it. An actual periscope is used and operated during the tests. The pool is a 45-foot-

Courtesy Miratel Electronics, Inc.

Fig. 8-3. The monitoring position of the closed-circuit television system used at an aerospace medical center.

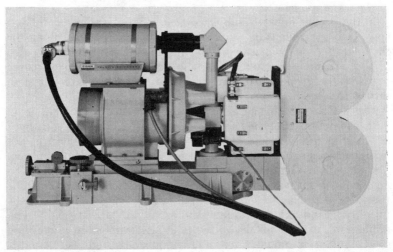

Courtesy Cohu/KinTel Electronics

Fig. 8-4. Optical boresight tracking equipment used with radar apparatus for tracking and photographing the flight of experimental space vehicles.

deep circular chamber and permits handling under-ice submarine equipment and instruments for measurements of breaking strength and acoustical properties of sea ice. The hatch in Fig. 8-6 permits a diver to gain access to equipment under the ice, which can be formed to 7-foot thicknesses.

Courtesy Cohu/KinTel Electronics

Fig. 8-5. A closed-circuit TV camera in a stainless steel housing at the bottom of an arctic experimental pool.

The control center at United Technology Corporation's solid-propellant rocket test area at the UTC Development and Test Center near Morgan Hill, California, is shown in Fig. 8-7. While tests are being observed by the remotely controlled camera, data are recorded permanently by means of a multichannel instrumentation system. The camera is enclosed in an environmental housing on a pan-and-tilt unit. Control is provided for remote-focus and iris settings. Resolution of the system is 650 lines.

Fig. 8-8 is a block diagram of a closed-circuit television system used for danger-point viewing of missile launching. Microwave equipment or coaxial cables may be used to interconnect camera

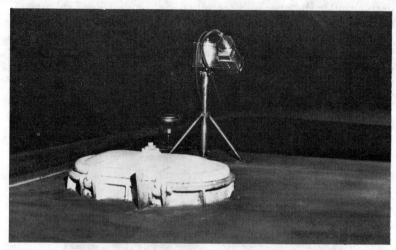

Courtesy Cohu/KinTel Electronics

Fig. 8-6. View of the "arctic" pool from behind the TV camera.

Courtesy Cohu/KinTel Electronics

Fig. 8-7. Control for solid-propellant rocket tests at United Technology Corporation.

and monitor positions. Long-length coaxial cables may require the use of line amplifiers as signal boosters.

Missile surveillance by closed-circuit television is an important phase of operations at Cape Kennedy, Florida. Four cameras are used to monitor Air Force firings. One camera is on top of the blockhouse; a second is on a dolly or on a swinging arm at the 11th level of the gantry; the third is at the approach ramp to

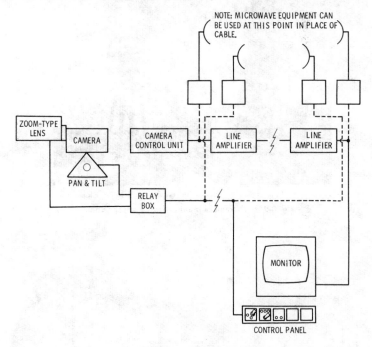

Fig. 8-8. A typical closed-circuit television equipment setup for safety-point monitoring of missile launches.

the gantry; and the fourth camera (Fig. 8-9) is at the "pull back" area 100 feet from the gantry. Fig. 8-10 shows a close up view of this camera. It is enclosed in an explosion-resistant housing atop a pan-and-tilt unit.

A view of the instrumentation room for the Atlas firings is given in Fig. 8-11. The monitors for the 4 cameras are suspended from the ceiling to give all operators an unobstructed view of the television images.

An unusual application for closed-circuit television has been developed by space scientists at General Dynamics Astronautics. A spacecraft-rendezvous simulator uses a TV monitor in the

Courtesy Cohu/KinTel Electronics

Fig. 8-9. A TV camera monitor for an Atlas firing.

Courtesy Cohu/KinTel Electronics

Fig. 8-10. Closeup view of camera pictured in Fig. 8-9.

"space vehicle." The monitor is positioned to replace the porthole. The TV camera is fitted with a special zoom lens. The camera photographs a model of the target vehicle which the astronaut is "approaching." The model vehicle can be seen in front of the monitor at Fig. 8-12. The "astronaut" and the "porthole" are shown in Fig. 8-13. Rendezvous maneuvers are simulated to provide development of techniques that may later be used in closing in on and locking with another spacecraft in flight. The initial contact with the target vehicle is represented by a tiny pinpoint of light on the monitor screen, indicating the target is far distant. As the two vehicles draw closer together, the magnification of the zoom lens is increased until the target vehicle appears to be only a few feet away. Computers determine the rate at which the target vehicle image increases in size. The zoom lens has a magnification and reduction capability of 1:5,000.

When the spacecraft is "returning to earth," the planet appears as a tiny spot, gradually increasing in size in accordance with the rate of re-entry. At touchdown the earth appears to be only a few feet from the spacecraft "porthole." A three-axis hand controller enables the astronaut to simulate flight of the spacecraft through pitch, yaw, and roll in response to problems fed into the instruments from a computer.

Courtesy Cohu/KinTel Electronics

Fig. 8-11. Monitors for four TV cameras in the instrumentation room of the Atlas test area.

Under a military contract, a new observation system for use at underwater depths to 1,000 feet has been developed. Entirely experimental, its purpose is to evaluate the different modes of underwater illumination and to compare photographic versus video operations. A spread-U–shaped structure (Fig. 8-14) holds a TV camera with a 10:1 zoom lens, a 35-mm film camera with a 10:1 zoom lens, and two sets of light sources. The lights are adjustable in position on the structure for a spread of approximately 8

Courtesy Cohu/KinTel Electronics

Fig. 8-12. Originating point of the simulator for space vehicle rendezvous control.

feet. The spread-U structure can be lowered by crane from a ship, holding the cameras in any orientation, looking straight down, straight up, and horizontally. The remote controls for the lights and both cameras are shown in the specially designed rack in Fig. 8-15. Fig. 8-16 shows a closeup of the pressure bell (with the front cover removed) that houses the TV camera.

MEDICINE

Medical electronics is rapidly gaining acceptance among the members of the medical profession. In fact, it is rapidly approaching the point where, because of increasing uses in the examining, operating, and recovery rooms, it may very well become a new profession or a specialty among doctors.

Closed-circuit television systems have also made important contributions to medical science. Applications for television in educational institutions, including medical schools, have already been illustrated in detail. Some of the uses attributed to educational applications obviously pertain as well to medical research and diagnostics. For example, enlargements via a TV camera and large-screen monitor in conjunction with a laboratory microscope to facilitate counts and in tissue analysis can be used for diagnosis. It is sometimes difficult to draw the line that indicates where medical research and practice begin and end.

Operating rooms are significant beneficiaries of closed-circuit television systems. In one application the camera is focused on the electrocardiograph trace during open heart surgery. Both the surgeon and the anesthetist require constant access to the informa-

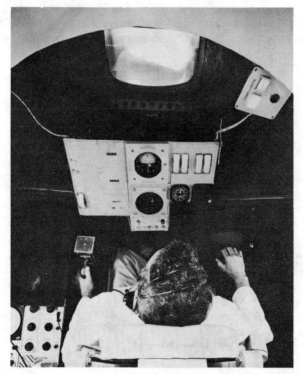

Courtesy Cohu/KinTel Electronics

Fig. 8-13. The "astronaut" in "outer space" practicing vehicle rendezvous by viewing a TV monitor serving as a porthole.

Courtesy Cohu/KinTel Electronics

Fig. 8-14. A special structure which supports a TV camera, 35-mm film camera, and lights for underwater observation.

tion shown on the graph. The graph is displayed on large-screen TV monitors in plain view of the operating team. Thus, both the convenience of an easy view of the EKG trace and the enlarged view of that trace are provided at once. In operating room installations, monitors must be installed in explosionproof housings be-

Courtesy Cohu/KinTel Electronics

Fig. 8-15. Control panel and a monitor for the underwater observation equipment of Fig. 8-14.

cause of the combustible atmosphere created by the anesthesia and oxygen used during surgical procedures. The housing prevents any arcing within the monitor from causing ignition.

Fluoroscopy, an important tool for the radiologist, gains new performance levels and utility when used with closed-circuit television. Conventionally the radiologist uses an image intensifier to enable a reduction in the radiation to which a patient may have to be exposed for long periods of time while undergoing surgery. In practice it is the responsibility of the radiologist to continuously view the fluoroscoped organs and advise the surgeon. A television camera at the image intensifier can be used to feed fluoroscope pictures to a large-screen monitor at the operating table for the surgeon and another at the radiologist's position for eye relief. This practice offers several advantages; the need for voice communications with the inherent possibility of misinterpretation is reduced, and the contrast and brightness controls at the camera and monitor enable extraordinary improvements in intensity of the fluoroscope image, making possible further reduc-

Courtesy Cohu/KinTel Electronics

Fig. 8-16. A view of the TV camera of Fig. 8-14 with the front cover of the pressure bell removed.

Courtesy Sylvania Electric Products, Inc.

Fig. 8-17. A TV monitor at the nurses station in a hospital.

tions in the required intensity of radiation exposure. The radiologist continues as before to be responsible for the fluoroscope.

A closed-circuit television system with fine-line definition capabilities can be used to transmit special data such as X-ray negatives from the developing room to the operating room where the surgical team may be waiting to make an evaluation before proceeding. Thus time is saved in transportation and also by eliminating the need for thorough drying of the negative.

The surgical amphitheater may be replaced by closed-circuit television. Cameras can be simultaneously focused on instruments, surgeons, and the patient to provide large audiences of doctors and students with extraordinary views. The commentary from the operating room can be carried over separate lines with a microphone at one end and speakers at the other.

Hospital wards and private rooms can be equipped with television cameras. Monitors at the nurses' station (Fig. 8-17) provide continuous patient observation either by automatic switching at short prescribed intervals from camera to camera or by the installation of separate monitors for each camera. The latter is preferred where constant care has been ordered. Explosionproof housings must be used for cameras installed in a room where a patient is receiving oxygen.

Psychotherapists make excellent use of closed-circuit systems. At times the free actions of patients might become inhibited or restrained by the physical presence of the therapist and his associates. A remotely controlled pan-, tilt-, and zoom-equipped camera enables complete close observation without awareness on the part of the patient. In addition, the therapy team can engage in open discussion of the actions at the moment of occurrence without disturbing the patient.

Patients isolated in hospital rooms have been permitted to have "visitors" via closed-circuit television and voice intercom. Some "visits" (Fig. 8-18) can prove to be excellent boosters for the depressed spirits of those who are otherwise unable to see family, children, or friends. It is accepted that the attitude of a patient is an important factor in speeding the recovery during the post-operative period. A camera is placed in the lobby or an office of the hospital and fed by coaxial cable to the TV monitor in the patient's room. RF cameras are adequate for this type of service and offer the added advantage of being connectable directly to the entertainment TV set in the patient's room.

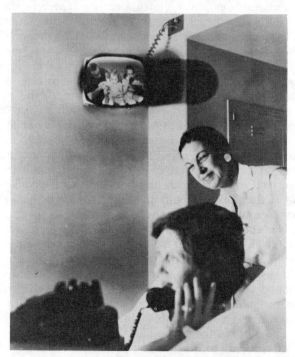

Courtesy Sylvania Electric Products, Inc.

Fig. 8-18. A patient "visiting" with her family via television.

Neurosurgeons have used cameras and monitors to observe a patient being treated by proton bombardment. Since anesthesia is required to prevent movement of the patient while pinpointing the proton beam on the radiosensitive tumor, constant observation of respiratory excursions and gas flows from the anesthesia is required. High radiation hazards in the treatment chamber make it necessary to leave the patient unattended during the treatment period. A TV camera in the chamber fitted with a pan–and–tilt mechanism and a zoom lens, all enclosed in a radiation-resistant camera housing, enables technicians and neurosurgeons to read flowmeters and observe the patient's rib cage or breathing bag while safely positioned outside the radiation area. In case of difficulty, the proton beam can be instantly interrupted and the room entered.

Psychiatrists at the Medical Center of the University of Mississippi have video-tape recorded interviews with patients. The original purpose was for staff education. However, it has proven useful in providing a pictorial record and an objective capability for determining whether or not real progress is being made with patients. Playing back and reviewing earlier tape recordings provides the individual psychiatrist with an accurate picture of the patient's responses. This has been carried still further. When a patient is initially admitted to the center, he is interviewed for 12 minutes by a psychiatrist who asks a series of predetermined questions. Subsequent weekly interviews are also tape recorded. By playing back the tapes to the patient himself, the patient is enabled to gain a careful self-evaluation capability. It is expected that this capability will lead to accelerated recovery or at least to rapid improvements in self-control.

Various two-way television techniques which could extend mental health services to areas remote from psychiatric centers have been experimented with at the Nebraska Psychiatric Institute. One of these experiments involves the use of closed-circuit television in group therapy. In the tests, patients in the group were seated in one room, the therapist in another; patients' chairs were arranged in a "V" formation, facing the television screen on which the therapist appeared. A camera mounted above the group's TV monitor transmitted the view of the group to the therapist, who was equipped with two monitors, one for viewing the group and the other for monitoring his own facial expressions. In a third room, two other monitors enabled the clinical investigator and a technician to observe the group and the therapist simultaneously, as well as to provide control for equipment operation.

Six sessions were conducted with each of four groups with the patients and therapists meeting only via television. As a control, four groups also met for six conventional (nontelevised) sessions. Before the first session, all the patients were shown the system and introduced to the technician and the clinical investigator because they would be witnessing the sessions. It was reported that the patients maintained only a short interest in the technical aspects of the system and, after the first session, seldom referred to the technique itself. The project was sponsored by the National Institute of Mental Health. It is interesting to note that, although the technique of closed-circuit television in this specific method of application is novel and of some value, the therapist as an individual remains the most important element in group therapy. That is to say, closed-circuit television systems offer certain technical advantages but do not replace the capabilities of the psychotherapist. The comprehensive closed-circuit television system in use at St. Christopher's Hospital, Philadelphia, Pennsylvania, is diagrammed at Fig. 8-19. It provides television facilities for use in all aspects of hospital examination, operation, instruction, and care.

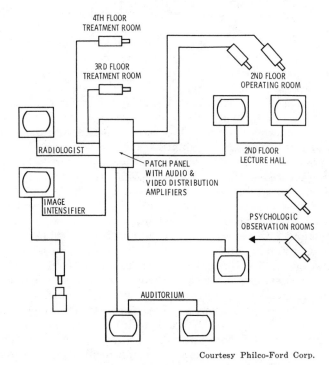

Courtesy Philco-Ford Corp.

Fig. 8-19. A diagram of the TV system at St. Christopher's Hospital, Philadelphia, Pennsylvania.

MILITARY

The mountain is brought to "Mohammed" with closed-circuit television; views of military encampments and battlefields can be televised to headquarters staffs located behind the lines. For this purpose a microwave relay is ideally suited as the transmitting medium. Scouting parties and small patrols can carry miniaturized cameras and transmitters, assuring the immediate return to the observation post or command unit of information essential to tactics. Thus, the potential of human error, subjective viewpoints, and verbal reports is eliminated. Closed-circuit systems perform excellent duty as "sentries" in surveillance of restricted areas as well as outposts. There are many uses for closed-circuit television systems in military installations. Due to the nature of the applications, details are lacking with regard to specific equipment and its uses. However, it is not classified information that the military makes heavy use of closed-circuit systems in education, research, medicine, and security—all of which have been described in their nonmilitary counterparts in previous chapters.

Aerial surveys and reconnaissance can make good use of television. Several cameras mounted on aircraft can "photograph" views of areas in wide angle and closeup simultaneously. Where it is not practicable to microwave relay the picture information directly from the aircraft to the ground station, video-tape recorders aboard the craft can make permanent recordings of the airborne views. These can then be played back immediately on landing for intelligence officers and other personnel involved in converting the information into strategy, tactics, and deployment of combat personnel and equipment.

Proposals have been made for statewide defense networks of airborne television cameras and microwave relay stations. Immediately following a battle action affecting civilian populations, the TV-equipped airborne stations would effect reconnaissance providing civilian defense and local military forces with accurate information with regard to devastation. The ordering of rescue teams, equipment, and whatever survival apparatus might be required to restore order would thus be greatly facilitated.

Naval vessels can use closed-circuit television for remote-controlled observation at the bridge and at communications centers. Strategically located cameras can give key persons views of invisible areas inside the vessel to aid in fire control, administration, and in channel and port navigation. Naval pilots are made less dependent on voice communications and hand signals in maneuvering a ship into a berth when TV cameras provide them with actual views of sides, bow, and stern.

Video intercoms enable off-duty officers to maintain "informal watches" on weather and shipboard activities. Propeller-shaft tunnels and areas of difficult access can be observed via television. Gauges and engine-room activities can be observed by the chief engineer at any time and location through the use of television. Underwater demolition and salvage crews can use compact TV cameras in special housings to relay information to the surface for determination of needs for special equipment and personnel.

Television brings field training a new dimension that enables instructors in war games to simultaneously view all aspects of the "battle" and the actions of individual leaders. By combining direct viewing with video tape recordings which are later played back, the debriefing sessions of commanders gain genuine substance, and an impact that assures significant improvements in field performance.

PUBLIC SERVICES

The patterns of parkways, bridge and tunnel approaches, highways, and other entrances and exits to the centers of cities have been almost impossible to police and survey with a reasonable force of men. The enormous increase in private ownership and usage of automobiles has created bottlenecks during peak traffic periods that cannot be rapidly and accurately understood and "broken." However, closed-circuit television cameras with their monitors located at central dispatching points provide immediate and advantageous views of any "bottlenecks." This makes it possible to efficiently dispatch any men and equipment necessary to resolve the specific situation.

Closed-circuit systems have been installed in tunnels, such as the Lincoln Tunnel in New York City. Placed at intervals of several hundred feet, TV cameras are equipped with mirrors and image splitters where it is desired to view two-way traffic with a single camera. The monitors are located at one end of the tunnel in a central dispatcher's office. Each camera has its own monitor, and should a vehicle breakdown occur inside the tunnel, the officer on TV watch can control traffic in individual lanes through a traffic light system. He then dispatches the necessary emergency equipment and personnel. This relieves police officers for other duties. Cameras are installed in weather-resistant housings to protect them from the caustic solution that is periodically sprayed on the interiors of the tunnel as a part of the regular cleaning schedule. The housings are mounted on vibration and shock-resistant devices as a protection against the damaging effects of the rumble of heavy vehicles and traffic.

On drawbridges, TV cameras show the operator the condition of approaches to both ends of the bridge, reducing manpower requirements and continuing the assurance of safety in operating the drawbridge.

The man-made complex of streets and thoroughfares that brings traffic into major cities demands continuous maintenance, improvement, repair, and re-evaluation. As a matter of routine and preventive maintenance, it is not unusual to periodically replace conduits that form the sewer, water, or gas lines buried underneath city streets because their interiors are not accessible for

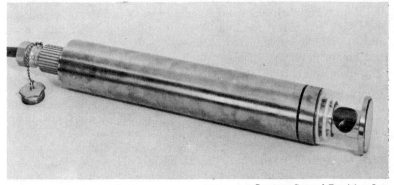

Courtesy General Precision, Inc.

Fig. 8-20. An underground-pipe camera.

visual inspection. The advent of closed-circuit television with its offerings of compact cameras and high-resolution picture transmission capabilities has, in many areas, completely revised the maintenance and inspection techniques, thus saving many man hours and expenses of operation. With the aid of compact cylindrical cameras enclosed in waterproof housings, inspections are made at widely separated points of entry to those conduits. The camera (Fig. 8-20) is either fed or dragged through the conduit. A mirror rotates on the axis of the camera lens as the camera moves forward. Thus, a 360° view of the pipe interior is available at a street-level monitor. Any cracks, holes, or breaks can be instantly spotted. From this inspection, officials can quickly determine which sections of the pipe are defective and need replacement. This significantly reduces the problems and costs related to major excavations at the street level. The housings of cameras used in such work are equipped with nonfogging windows and lenses. A cold-light source is affixed to the housing. This technique enables the exact locating of the defect in the conduit as a function of distance from the point of camera entry. Determination can then be made as to the nature of the trouble and whether sealing compound is adequate to effect the repair. Thus, closed-circuit television can, in some cases, entirely eliminate the need for an excavation of any kind.

Television cameras provided an unusual assistance in the construction of a $50,000,000 sewage system in California. Divers usually descend in such projects to guide each 6½- and 9-foot–diameter concrete pipe section into position with the previously laid section. TV cameras were affixed to the huge structure used to lower the massive concrete pipes. A mercury-vapor lamp provided illumination. The monitor showed engineers on the surface if the pipe was lined up properly, as indicated by marks of black paint, thus assisting the diver in making efficient use of his dive time. At 200-foot depths, murky waters often reduced the visibility of the diver to zero, halting all diving operations until the water cleared. It became quite costly to send a diver down to the 200-foot level to determine visibility conditions at frequent intervals. An interestingly simple solution was devised using the TV camera equipment already on hand. Camera and mercury-vapor lamps were lowered with a length of pipe on which calibrated distance markers were painted. By reading the markers on the pipe as seen on the TV monitor, it was possible to determine subsurface visibility and whether or not it was practical to resume diving and pipe-laying operations. In at least one case, additional time and expense were saved by using a helicopter to make the trip to the diving location to lower the camera, lights, and calibrated pipe, eliminating the need for time-consuming boat trips.

Police departments have been experimenting with closed-circuit television at the morning lineup. Monitors at widely separated precincts enable personnel to "attend" without leaving their station houses. A considerable saving in travel time for police personnel results.

The Massachusetts Prison at Walpole has used television surveillance of the main corridor as a means for backing up the solitary guards as they approach the locked prison gates. The House of Detention for Men, Brooklyn, New York, has used closed-circuit television to permit the warden to instantly inspect the kitchen and butcher shop, the yard, and principal corridors. After being alerted by telephone or intercom, the warden switches his monitor to the TV camera located in the trouble zone and is able to instantly evaluate the situation.

Experiments have been conducted with prison authorities with regard to cell-block surveillance during "lights off" hours when the number of guards on duty may be reduced. While it is claimed by some that the rights of authorities to observe the interiors of cells on a continuous basis are questionable, it is sometimes essential in maximum-security cells to provide some means for constant surveillance of specific prisoners. A portable television camera and monitor at the guard desk fulfills the surveillance requirement without making it necessary for a guard to be posted directly outside the cell in question.

Courtesy General Precision, Inc.

Fig. 8-21. A TV camera fitted in a special housing and lens assembly for monitoring the interior of a furnace.

The need for a means for continuous surveillance of security vestibules and work and play areas in corrective institutions is recognized by all. Closed-circuit television is gaining recognition as being an efficient method for accomplishing this. When determining equipment for such installations, concern must be given to the widely varying ambient light conditions over the 24-hour period. Cameras for such installations must have automatic light compensation capabilities in the order of at least 2,000:1 to eliminate the need for constant readjustment of the equipment.

The TV camera in Fig. 8-21 is enclosed in a specially designed housing and is fitted with a unique lens assembly to make it possible to observe the interior of a furnace. The lens assembly is approximately 11 inches long and protrudes partially into the furnace, where it is subjected to temperatures of 3,000°F and heavy slag conditions. Air under pressure is continuously purged into the furnace around the lens to keep the lens system clean and cool. The camera provides the operator in the main room with immediate information on burner and flame conditions. It can actually see more than can be seen by visual observation from the same location. This technique permits safe remote operation of large multiburner boilers. The photograph in Fig. 8-21 was taken at the Public Service Electric and Gas Company of New Jersey, which has an extensive closed-circuit television system.

Lenses, Lighting, and Wiring

I N PLANNING a closed-circuit television installation you can profit handsomely from a detailed understanding of some of the less obvious but extremely important factors that can affect the performance of the system. Equipment manufacturers have received complaints from customers who purchased the finest cameras and monitors available, with the report that after having completed the installation, the initial results were most disappointing. Investigation of such incidents by experienced field engineers most often shows that lighting technique was incorrect or inadequate, the background for the televised subject did not enable proper contrast control, or that incorrect lenses were being used. Too often the customer had relied on an analysis of the proposed application made with the naked eye.

It is easy to be misled if the unaided or inexperienced eye is allowed to evaluate a proposed television scene. A pair of eyes views a scene, perceives depth, and combines, with the unique ability of the mind to associate images and differentiate between subjects and backgrounds. Human vision has extraordinary capabilities of compensating for too much or too little contrast or scene illumination. The superbly ordered human mind can accept an optical situation and convert it into useful information. However, when a TV camera and monitor are interposed between the scene and the observer's eyes, an artificial element is introduced to the mind. The loss of depth perceptibility alone can sometimes create a problem in familiarity association for the mind.

If the televised scene is inadequately handled or the TV camera is poorly equipped with lenses, the observer may reject the unreal televised images; the mind is unable to accept the signals. The field engineers provided by the manufacturers are able to apply their experiences to such situations. After consultation and new demonstrations, they are usually able to set things right and enable the system owner to realize the full capabilities of the TV camera and its monitor. The following data and discussion of lenses, lighting, and other items are essential to systems planners. They are considerations based on the most common "faults" in performance reported by customers to field engineers assigned as troubleshooters. The least common "faults" are based on electronic troubles—thanks to the quality control practiced by equipment manufacturers.

LENSES

Incorrect lens selection for a vidicon TV camera can have a significantly deleterious effect on picture brightness, and contrast. When too "slow" a lens is used, it is entirely possible that the deficiency cannot be compensated with electronic adjustments at either the TV camera or the TV monitor. The basic problem is in the optics and not the electronics; either a faster lens must be used, or the scene illumination or background lighting must be modified. When the field of view provided by a lens is incorrect (too narrow or too wide), it becomes difficult to properly compose a scene, or it becomes impossible to view the subject with any satisfaction in a closeup or magnification arrangement. An unusually wide selection of lenses is available for use with vidicon cameras. They can be obtained at camera stores that handle motion-picture film accessories, or through the suppliers and manufacturers of TV equipment. In fact, as was pointed out earlier, lenses made for use with conventional 16-mm motion-picture film cameras are exactly the same as those used with vidicon-equipped closed-circuit television cameras.

A basic understanding of the practices of optics and lighting controls can be obtained without prior training or experience as an engineer. The knowledge can help prevent costly, time-consuming errors in installation.

Focal Length

The local length is the distance behind the optical center of the lens to the point where rays are focused. When an object at in-

Table 9-1. Fields of View

Distance from Lens to Subject in Feet	9.5mm (3/8")		12mm (31/64")		13mm (33/64")		25mm (1")		50mm (2")	
	Height	Width	Height	Width	Height	Width	Height	Width	Height	Width
2	1'-8"	2'-2"	1'-4"	1'-9"	1'-2"	1'-7"	0'-8"	0'-10"	0'-4"	0'-5"
3	2'-8"	3'-6"	2'-1"	2'-9"	1'-11"	2'-7"	1'-0"	1'-4"	0'-6"	0'-8"
4	3'-9"	4'-10"	2'-11"	3'-10"	2'-8"	3'-6"	1'-4"	1'-10"	0'-8"	0'-11"
5	4'-10"	6'-7"	3'-11"	5'-2"	3'-8"	4'-10"	1'-10"	2'-6"	0'-11"	1'-3"
6	5'-11"	7'-11"	4'-8"	6'-3"	4'-4"	5'-9"	2'-2"	3'-0"	1'-1"	1'-6"
7	6'-11"	9'-2"	5'-5"	7'-3"	5'-1"	6'-9"	2'-6"	3'-6"	1'-3"	1'-9"
8	7'-11"	10'-6"	6'-3"	8'-4"	5'-9"	7'-8"	3'-0"	4'-0"	1'-6"	2'-0"
9	8'-11"	11'-10"	7'-0"	9'-4"	6'-6"	8'-8"	3'-4"	4'-6"	1'-8"	2'-3"
10	9'-11"	13'-2"	7'-10"	10'-5"	7'-2"	9'-7"	3'-10"	5'-0"	1'-11"	2'-6"
12	11'-10"	15'-9"	9'-5"	12'-6"	8'-8"	11'-6"	4'-7"	6'-0"	2'-3"	3'-0"
14	13'-10"	18'-5"	10'-11"	14'-7"	10'-2"	13'-6"	5'-4"	7'-0"	2'-8"	3'-6"
16	15'-9"	21'-0"	12'-6"	16'-8"	11'-7"	15'-5"	6'-0"	8'-0"	3'-0"	4'-0"
18	17'-9"	23'-8"	14'-1"	18'-10"	13'-0"	17'-4"	6'-9"	9'-0"	3'-5"	4'-6"
20	19'-9"	26'-4"	15'-8"	20'-10"	14'-5"	19'-3"	7'-6"	10'-0"	3'-9"	5'-0"
25	24'-8"	32'-11"	19'-8"	26'-3"	18'-0"	24'-0"	9'-4"	12'-6"	4'-8"	6'-3"
30	29'-11"	39'-1"	23'-5"	31'-2"	21'-8"	28'-10"	11'-2"	15'-0"	5'-7"	7'-6"
35	34'-7"	46'-1"	27'-4"	36'-5"	25'-3"	33'-8"	13'-1"	17'-6"	6'-6"	8'-9"
40	39'-8"	52'-8"	31'-2"	41'-7"	28'-11"	38'-6"	15'-0"	20'-0"	7'-6"	10'-0"
45	44'-5"	59'-3"	35'-2"	46'-10"	32'-5"	43'-3"	16'-11"	22'-6"	8'-5"	11'-3"
50	49'-4"	65'-9"	39'-0"	52'-0"	36'-0"	48'-0"	18'-8"	25'-0"	9'-4"	12'-6"
60	59'-2"	78'-11"	46'-10"	62'-5"	43'-3"	57'-8"	22'-6"	30'-0"	11'-3"	15'-0"
70	69'-1"	92'-0"	54'-8"	72'-10"	50'-5"	67'-3"	26'-2"	35'-0"	13'-1"	17'-6"
80	78'-11"	105'-3"	62'-5"	83'-2"	57'-8"	76'-11"	30'-0"	40'-0"	15'-0"	20'-0"
90	88'-10"	118'-5"	70'-2"	93'-7"	64'-11"	86'-6"	33'-10"	45'-0"	16'-11"	22'-6"
100	98'-8"	131'-7"	78'-0"	104'-0"	72'-0"	96'-0"	37'-6"	50'-0"	18'-9"	25'-0"

Table 9-1. Fields of View (continued)

Distance from Lens to Subject in Feet	75mm (3") Height	75mm (3") Width	102mm (4") Height	102mm (4") Width	125mm (5") Height	125mm (5") Width	150mm (6") Height	150mm (6") Width	200mm (8") Height	200mm (8") Width
2	0'-3"	0'-4"	0'-2"	0'-3"	0'-1"	0'-2"	—	—	—	—
3	0'-4"	0'-6"	0'-3"	0'-5"	0'-2"	0'-3"	—	—	—	—
4	0'-6"	0'-8"	0'-4"	0'-6"	0'-3"	0'-4"	—	—	—	—
5	0'-8"	0'-10"	0'-6"	0'-8"	0'-4"	0'-6"	—	—	—	—
6	0'-9"	1'-0"	0'-7"	0'-9"	0'-5"	0'-7"	0'-4"	0'-6"	—	—
7	0'-10"	1'-2"	0'-8"	0'-11"	0'-6"	0'-8"	0'-5"	0'-7"	—	—
8	1'-0"	1'-4"	0'-9"	1'-0"	0'-7"	0'-10"	0'-6"	0'-8"	—	—
9	1'-1"	1'-6"	0'-10"	1'-2"	0'-8"	0'-11"	0'-6"	0'-9"	—	—
10	1'-3"	1'-8"	0'-11"	1'-3"	0'-9"	1'-0"	0'-7"	0'-10"	—	—
12	1'-6"	2'-0"	1'-1"	1'-6"	0'-11"	1'-2"	0'-9"	1'-0"	0'-6"	0'-9"
14	1'-9"	2'-4"	1'-4"	1'-9"	1'-1"	1'-5"	0'-11"	1'-2"	0'-6"	0'-9"
16	2'-0"	2'-8"	1'-6"	2'-0"	1'-2"	1'-7"	1'-0"	1'-4"	0'-9"	1'-0"
18	2'-3"	3'-0"	1'-8"	2'-3"	1'-4"	1'-10"	1'-2"	1'-6"	0'-10"	1'-1"
20	2'-6"	3'-4"	1'-10"	2'-6"	1'-6"	2'-0"	1'-3"	1'-8"	0'-11"	1'-3"
25	3'-2"	4'-2"	2'-4"	3'-2"	1'-10"	2'-6"	1'-7"	2'-1"	1'-2"	1'-7"
30	3'-9"	5'-0"	2'-10"	3'-9"	2'-3"	3'-0"	1'-10"	2'-6"	1'-4"	1'-10"
35	4'-5"	5'-10"	3'-3"	4'-5"	2'-8"	3'-6"	2'-2"	2'-11"	1'-8"	2'-3"
40	5'-0"	6'-8"	3'-9"	5'-0"	3'-0"	4'-0"	2'-6"	3'-4"	1'-10"	2'-6"
45	5'-8"	7'-6"	4'-3"	5'-8"	3'-5"	4'-6"	2'-10"	3'-9"	2'-2"	2'-10"
50	6'-3"	8'-4"	4'-9"	6'-3"	3'-9"	5'-0"	3'-2"	4'-2"	2'-4"	3'-1"
60	7'-6"	10'-0"	5'-8"	7'-6"	4'-6"	6'-0"	3'-9"	5'-0"	2'-10"	3'-9"
70	8'-9"	11'-8"	6'-7"	8'-9"	5'-3"	7'-0"	4'-5"	5'-10"	3'-4"	4'-5"
80	10'-0"	13'-4"	7'-6"	10'-0"	6'-0"	8'-0"	5'-0"	6'-8"	3'-9"	5'-0"
90	11'-3"	15'-0"	8'-5"	11'-3"	6'-9"	9'-0"	5'-7"	7'-6"	4'-2"	5'-7"
100	12'-6"	16'-8"	9'-4"	12'-6"	7'-6"	10'-0"	6'-3"	8'-4"	4'-8"	6'-3"

Courtesy Radio Corporation of America

finity distance from the lens is focused onto a screen located exactly 1 inch behind the lens, the focal length is said to be 1 inch. Focal length is designated by the capital letter F. The F of a lens governs the size of the image and therefore the angle of the field covered. The longer the focal length or the larger the F number designated on the lens, the greater is the magnification of the image, assuming the image being viewed is at a fixed distance from the optical center of the lens. It is the focal length and not the type of lens that determines the size of the picture formed on the screen. The diameter and thickness of a lens are both factors that affect its focal length. Increasing both the diameter and the thickness of the lens decreases the focal length.

Table 9-1 gives the sizes of the fields of view encompassed for lenses of different focal lengths, with the objects placed at varying distances from the camera lens. With this table and an estimation of expected work or areas to be surveyed by the camera, you can specify and order the proper lens F.

The aspect ratio for standard television receivers, monitors, and cameras is 3 units high by 4 units wide. A mask is fitted over the face of the camera tube to ensure the transmission of pictures in this ratio. This mask prevents confusion when an electronic viewfinder is used. Without it more picture area than the monitor can use might be transmitted. Thus the horizontal field is wider by 4:3, or 1.3 times the vertical field; and the vertical field is 3:4, or 0.75 times the horizontal field. Since the usable area on the tube surface is proportional to the field to be viewed, the following formula can be used to compute any distance or field for any lens of known focal length:

$$FW = wD$$

where,
 F is the focal length in inches,
 W is the width of field in feet,
 D is the distance to object in feet,
 w is the width of usable tube surface in inches ($w = 0.5$ inch for a 1-inch vidicon tube).

To find the height, multiply W by 0.75. Of course, the formula can be used to compute any unknown quantity. If, for example, you have a lens of known focal length and want to know how far from the camera you would have to place the object to achieve a given horizontal field of view, the formula becomes:

$$D = \frac{FW}{w}$$

If you want to determine what focal length of lens is needed to view a field of known size, the formula is

$$F = \frac{wD}{W}$$

Lens Speed

The speed, or ability of a lens to "collect" light, is another important characteristic. The speed of a lens is designated by the small letter f and is derived from the formula:

$$f = \frac{F}{d}$$

where,

    F is the focal length,
    d is the lens diameter.

It can be seen that the lens diameter is inversely proportional to the f number for a given focal length. Obviously, a lens of a large diameter admits more light than one of a smaller diameter. A lens with a large diameter and with a small f number is considered to be "fast." The smaller the f number the faster the lens. Typical fast lenses such as those used with closed-circuit television cameras have f speed ratings of $f: 1.5$ and $f: 1.9$. It is not uncommon, however, to find many cameras intended for daylight operation to be equipped with $f: 4.5$ lenses.

Television lenses are generally fitted with an adjustable iris or diaphragm which is used to change the effective diameter of the lens. Thus a mechanical adjustment for varying conditions of reflected light is provided. The speed of a lens is rated at its widest "stop" or largest lens diameter. Because the diaphragm is located at a nodal point in the lens (where the light rays cross or become inverted), the field of view is not affected by diaphragm settings.

Generally, lenses with longer focal lengths have high f ratings; thus, they are slower in speed. This is readily understood when the costly grinding process necessary to produce a high-quality large-diameter lens is considered. The amount of light passed through a lens varies inversely with the square of the f number rating. For example, if the iris stop is changed from $f: 2$ to $f: 4$, a ratio of 2, the amount of light admitted is not $1/2$; it is the square of $\frac{1}{2}$, or $\frac{1}{4}$. Thus, $\frac{1}{4}$ of the light passed at $f: 2$ is passed at $f: 4$.

Depth of Field

The depth of field is the area that is plainly in focus, both ahead of and behind the subject whose image is being impressed on the

photosensitive screen area of the TV camera pickup tube. As the
f number of the lens is increased, the depth of field in which objects remain in focus increases. As the focal length increases, the
depth of field decreases. The closer an object is to the lens, the
shorter is the depth of field, and the more critical the need for accurate focusing. In general, for a given lens, short focal length,
small iris openings, and great distances between the camera and
objects combine to give maximum depth of field.

Zoom Lens

Electrically controlled zoom lenses, such as the one pictured in
Fig. 9-1, have miniature motors to provide remote-control adjustments for changing the focal length, focus, and iris of the lens

Courtesy Zoomar, Inc.

Fig. 9-1. An electrically controlled zoom lens.

assembly. Nylon gears assure quiet, vibration-free movement.
The three miniature motors of the zoom lens assembly are pictured in Fig. 9-2. From left to right, the motors control iris, zoom
or focal length, and focus. The assembly shown here is normally
enclosed in a housing similar to those shown in Fig. 9-3. Each of
these lenses has a different range of focal lengths. The wiring
diagram for the lens unit and control box of the zoom lens shown
in Figs. 9-1 and 9-2 is given in Fig. 9-4. The use of a DC power
supply and DC motors permits the direction of rotation of the
three motors to be reversed for opening and closing the iris,
zooming in and out, and focusing for near and far objects. The
controls are not calibrated. The lens is actuated while the picture
is monitored. Voltage losses incurred even when the power line
is as far as a 2-mile distance from its connection can be compensated for by the tapped transformer primary. This tapped primary
also provides a variable speed control for the three motors.

Courtesy Zoomar, Inc.

Fig. 9-2. Miniature motors for operating the zoom lens assembly in Fig. 9-1.

SCENE LIGHTING

Light for the subject to be televised should be one of the foremost considerations in the system plan. The image seen on the monitor is entirely a function of the reflected light from the scene with respect to any limitations the TV camera might impose on the system. The assumption here is that the camera selected is designed to perform under widely varying lighting conditions. However, when we discuss "proper scene light," we are concerned with obtaining optimum performance as seen on a high-quality video monitor. It must be pointed out again that even the finest TV camera and monitor equipment ever commercially produced cannot be expected to entirely compensate for poorly handled basic lighting.

Courtesy Zoomar, Inc.

Fig. 9-3. Zoom lenses enclosed in housings.

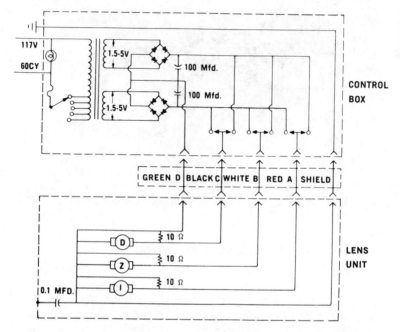

Courtesy Zoomar, Inc.

Fig. 9-4. Wiring diagram for the lens pictured in Figs. 9-1 and 9-2.

The Nature of Light

An understanding of the nature of light will clarify the philosophy and techniques employed in television lighting. The visible light that can be seen by the unaided human eye is a very small part of the spectrum of electromagnetic energy. Directly above and below this portion of the spectrum are infrared light and ultraviolet light, neither of which is visible to the human eye without some form of energy conversion.

The unit of measurement of a wavelength of light is the *angstrom*. An *angstrom* is equal to one ten-millionth of a millimeter, or approximately four billionths of an inch. Sometimes the *micron* is used as the unit to express light wavelength. A micron is one millionth of a meter, or 10^4 angstroms. The *footcandle* is frequently encountered in discussions and descriptions of light. One footcandle is the intensity of illumination on a surface one foot from a uniform source of one candlepower. The *lumen* is the unit of luminous flux. A *footlambert* is a unit of reflected light or emitted light, whereas the footcandle is a unit of incident light. If the surface at which the light arrives is a perfect diffuser and perfect reflector, the footcandle and the footlambert become of the same value.

Brightness is reflected light or intensity of illumination resulting from a density of luminous flux on a surface. *Contrast* is the degree of difference in tone between object and background. and is measured in terms of gamma, a numerical indicator of degree of contrast. Visually it is witnessed as a distinct separation between white and dark areas in the televised scene as viewed at the monitor. When the contrast is poor, the picture appears gray and "washed out."

Illumination and Brightness

The amount of illumination required to achieve the desired televised brightness is dependent on the scene to be televised. That is, scenes which are largely composed of white or light colors (good reflectors) require much less illumination than scenes that are composed of dark colors. In addition, the spectral response of the vidicon must be considered. Different scenes with identical illumination will have different brightness due to changes in light reflected back to the lens. A light striking a plane at a given angle will be reflected at the same angle. Scene lights must be arranged to reflect light toward the camera lens, a relatively small target area.

When lights cannot be located at the camera position, care should be taken that their housings are out of the field of view. Scene illumination decreases as the square of the distance of the source of light to the scene. This is not apparent to the human eye with its extraordinary ability to adjust rapidly to a wide variation of light intensities. A light meter should be used whenever possible to measure brightness by pointing the meter at the camera from within the same area.

Generally, the more light there is, the better the picture will be; this will allow stopping the lens down, which increases the depth of field and decreases the possibility of accidental burning of the vidicon. Increasing light levels that are very low will also improve contrast. If possible, backgrounds should never be brighter than the main subject. Pastels or dull paints are the best backgrounds. White or glossy backgrounds should be avoided. Both incandescent and fluorescent light sources work quite well with vidicon cameras.

Highlights

Whenever possible, the camera should not be aimed directly into bright lights because the target area of the vidicon might be permanently damaged. On cameras whose circuitry includes automatic light compensation, the camera will adjust to a level above the dark areas, thereby increasing the sensitivity in the low-light regions.

Bright lights may also cause black smears due to amplifier overload in the camera. This seriously affects the picture detail and the gray scale of tonal values. If the camera is held rigid in a constant-view position, the target may be burned unevenly by exposure to scenes of high contrast with strong highlights. Windows should be kept behind or to the sides of the camera whenever possible. If flames, light bulbs, or other self-luminescent objects are included in the scene, light filters or a light background will enable control of the total light impressed on the vidicon through the proper use of the adjustable iris.

When mirrors or other highly reflective surfaces are part of the scene, they should be treated with a nonreflective material, such as spray wax. Another approach is to use polarized light filters at the lens and at the light source, rotated until minimum reflections or glare are reproduced at the monitor location.

When it is necessary to view small or dark objects, spotlights are useful. They are available in many sizes; some are ideally suited for use in small confined areas, such as table tops. If the objects are too small for such an approach to lighting, treating them with a flat white paint or, in the case of small gauges, meters, coins, and stamps, taped markings may facilitate reading the information.

High Versus Low Lighting Levels

Lighting in the lower levels of 10 to 40 footcandles does not usually require any lighting to supplement the existing room lighting conditions. Most present-day offices and modern classrooms are designed for a lighting level of 50 footcandles. The higher levels, 100 footcandles and up, are obtained by using standard theatrical or TV-type spotlights and floodlights.

To determine if existing and ordinary room lighting, which may be a combination of incandescent and fluorescent permanently mounted fixtures, should be used, the telecaster has to consider the quality of the resulting picture and the standard he sets as acceptable for transmission. For example, if there is motion in the scene, either of the objects in the scene or of the camera itself (panning and tilting), and if it does not matter if the picture is somewhat grainy in appearance, low-level lighting is adequate. If, however, the scene contains moving objects, or the camera is required to pan and tilt at fast rates, high-level lighting must be used. Needless to say, commercial-TV broadcast operations always use the highest feasible light level to assure optimum picture transmission quality. Closed-circuit telecasters usually need high-quality picture transmission from scenes that contain a modest amount of motion.

Lighting Practices

Optimum levels of light can readily be obtained from incandescent spots and floods. The spotlights are usually the "Fresnel" type, which allows for the rapid insertion and removal of color filters. Fresnels are available in sizes up to 10,000 watts. The principal type of floodlight used in television work is the "scoop," so called because it resembles an old-fashioned sugar scoop. Lamps up to 2,000 watts can be used in scoops.

Fixture Mounting

Lighting units may be mounted on telescopic floor stands with swivel-type rubber-tired casters. However, this arrangement is usually employed only in portable or temporary setups. With this type of arrangement, extension cables are required to feed each floor stand. Since these extension cables must lie on the floor, and the stands require considerable space, serious problems are encountered when the camera must be moved about the studio.

To avoid the problems of floor congestion and mobility restrictions, it is recommended that the lights be hung from an overhead grid system in a permanent installation. The overhead grids should be fitted with an electrical distribution system with numerous outlets attached to it. Fig. 9-5 shows a plan for an overhead

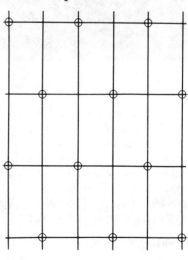

Fig. 9-5. Overhead grid plan using 1¼-inch pipe.

⊕ = AC OUTLET

grid measuring 20 feet by 24 feet. It consists of lengths of 1¼-inch pipe on 4-foot and 8-foot centers. The AC power receptacles are located for maximum utility. Lighting fixtures can be hung from the gridwork on pantographs so that the height of the individual fixtures can be varied. Clamps can be used to secure the pantograph to the overhead pipes, thereby making it possible to regroup or reposition the fixtures at will.

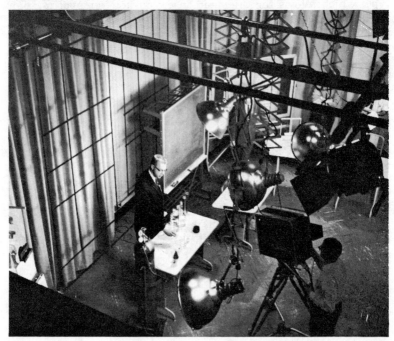

Courtesy Radio Corporation of America

Fig. 9-6. View through overhead grid into studio.

A track system could be devised of I-beams that would permit the lights to be rolled along the tracks, while permitting the entire track holding several sets of lights to be moved from point to point. A pole, handled from the floor, is all that is needed to move such a track-mounted setup. Fig. 9-6 is a view through such an overhead grid system into a studio in use. The floods are suspended from pantographs. A spotlight with barn doors is visible at the right edge of the picture.

Lighting Procedure

After the lighting method is incorporated in the system plan, the location of the lighting units and the method of directing them at the scene should be considered. The basic lighting for a technically good picture can be provided by the even application of light with floodlights, such as scoops. An adequate amount of light can be obtained by setting up a flood or spot on either side of and close to the camera. However, this produces flat and uninteresting scene lighting. A more textured, exciting picture can be obtained by using additional types of fixtures or ancillaries in conjunction with the floods and spots.

Locating and Aiming Lights

When lights are being set up, it is good practice to start with the *key* or *modeling light*. This principal source of directional illumination is often obtained from Fresnel spotlights. These are usually located and pointed so as to make a 20 to 40° angle with an imaginary horizontal line drawn at the eye level of the actor or through the center of the point of interest. Fresnels may be equipped with a frame to hold a masking device, called a "barn door." This device fits in front of the lens and is used to limit the horizontal and vertical spread of the light beam.

Back lighting comes next. Back lights are also normally Fresnel spots equipped with barn doors to prevent the light from spilling into the camera lens. They are mounted or, preferably, hung behind the subject and aimed to make a 45° vertical angle with the head and shoulders of the subject to be illuminated. Back light can vary in intensity from one half to twice that of the key light. This depends on the color of the hair and clothing of the subject. At this point in the lighting, the human eye might indicate the scene is well lit, but this will not be true when the scene is viewed through the "eye" of the TV camera.

Fill light, sometimes called base light, is needed. Fill light reduces the contrast between the very dark areas of the picture and the light areas produced by the key and back lighting. This contrast range should be kept somewhere between the ranges of 10:1 and 20:1. If we were trying to achieve a 15:1 contrast range, the darkest area or deepest shadow would have a reflected luminance that would be 1/15 that of the brighest object in the scene. Fill light is normally obtained by locating scoops in front of the scene and aiming them to make a 12 to 15° angle with an imaginary horizontal line at the eye level of the subject. Since this angle means the fill lights will be positioned much lower than the other lights, adjustable extensions, such as pantographs, are extremely useful when the scoops are hung from an overhead grid.

Set lights are the next consideration in a properly illuminated scene. They are the background lighting separate from that provided for principal subjects or areas. Set lighting is used to assist in decorating, mood setting, or providing additional dimension to the set. Scoops, Fresnels with barn doors, and pattern projectors are also used.

Pattern projectors can give great depth and dimension to a set consisting of nothing but a bare flat wall. For example, projecting a Venetian-blind pattern on the wall gives the impression that the sun is shining through a window, and casting a shadow on the background. Slides with different patterns are manufactured for unusual effects.

Balancing for Contrast

It is important to have the proper balance between the four types of light units described. If, for example, the set is painted in a light color so that it reflects more light than the flesh of the actor, skin tones may look darker than desired in the picture. This situations calls for a reduction in the set light. Spun-glass fabric can be used as diffuser material to reduce the set light. Because it is heat resistant and fireproof, spun-glass fabric is ideally suited for mounting directly on the light fixture close to the lamp itself. This material is available in rolls or sheets and is easily cut to fit the light unit. A single .015-inch thickness cuts about 20% of the light. Additional thicknesses can be used until the desired contrast is achieved, as viewed on the monitor and not with the naked eye. If the fill light is brighter than the key light, spun-glass fabric can be used to solve the problem. Of course, if the installation includes dimmer controls, the various lights can be individually balanced until the desired contrast is achieved. Dimmer controls are used as standard practice in theatrical and commercial television work.

Lighting and Image Retention

Vidicon tubes exhibit a phenomenon called *image retention*. This phenomenon is also known as sticking, streaking, trailing, smear, and lag. It occurs when the actor moves quickly or the camera is panned or tilted rapidly to a new position. It is especially noticeable in low-level lighting and becomes less apparent as the light level is increased. However, an increase in light is not always desirable; therefore, the following procedure should be followed to reduce image retention to a minimum:

1. Use an iris stop setting of $f:8$ and a lighting level of 250 footcandles of incident light measured with the light meter located at the object being televised and with the photocell

pointed toward the lens of the camera. The meter generally used in TV work is the same as that obtained from photo supply stores and used primarily for motion-picture photography. The semispherical light-meter attachment is never used in TV. The flat disc over the photocell is used. It is highly desirable to make use of a good-quality footcandle meter. However, with a little practice the markings on the motion-picture meter can be related to TV use.

2. As a general rule, open the camera lens as far as is practicable without seriously affecting the depth of field necessary to the picture. This has the effect of increasing the light level and reducing lag.

3. If the depth of field is affected by the use of a wide-open lens, a stop of $f:5.6$ may be used with a reduction in the contrast lighting on the set. The overall contrast range of $20:1$ may prove to be excessive; the reduction of image retention may be improved with a contrast range of $10:1$ or less. If the high contrast range is due to heavily contrasting set colors, steps should be taken to rectify this by repainting or changing the background materials. For example, a performer wearing a dark suit over a white shirt can easily exceed the $20:1$ contrast range, and there will be a blurred outline where the shirt is adjacent to the suit; quite probably, there will also be streaking when the performer moves. It is preferable that performers wear a blue shirt and gray tie when wearing a dark suit.

It is interesting to note that some closed-circuit television installations are operating very nicely without knowledge of lighting techniques and without standard lighting fixtures such as those described here. However, the budgets in some instances do not allow for such fixtures, so the telecasters must make do with conventional room lighting or with reinforced incandescent or fluorescent lighting. The problem of image retention or sticking has not really been solved. It has been avoided by instructing directors to keep action in the presentation down to a minimum and to avoid panning and tilting wherever possible. With or without a comprehensive lighting capability in the system, each lighting designer or director develops his own style and makes variations on the basic steps to suit his particular needs.

POWER REQUIREMENTS

It is obvious that electrical wiring of adequate capacity to carry the current for the lighting and the electronic systems must be provided. Cameras and monitors are, in varying degrees, sensitive to variations in line voltage. Severe variations in voltage can cause changes in electrical focus and in brightness, causing pictures to suddenly become blurry and contrast to change significantly. It is highly recommended that separate power lines be brought into the facility for the cameras and, if possible, for the monitors. This would help prevent changes in line voltages at the cameras and monitors as the lighting is varied in the studio during a telecast. In industrial and research television, separate power lines will isolate the camera and monitor from severe line-voltage changes and transients as machinery and other electrical apparatus are started and stopped. In installations where cameras are on 24-hour surveillance duty, separate lines should be drawn to isolate the cameras from changes in the load on the lines as shifts shut down or start up and as outdoor floodlights are illuminated during darkness hours. The problem can sometimes be eliminated, or at least reduced, where it is not feasible to bring in separate power lines, through the use of line-voltage regulators at the camera and at the monitor. A separate regulator should be provided for each unit of television equipment to assure the best results.

Experience indicates that it is wise to estimate power needs at up to 40 watts per square foot of studio floor. Meters should be provided for each leg of the wiring circuit and located within view of the lighting operator. He can monitor the meters to make sure that limits will not be exceeded and cause fuses or circuit breakers to actuate while the telecast is in progress.

A master control panel should be provided for the entire studio light arrangement. A master switch is desirable to enable complete "black-outs" where they might be required as part of a presentation. Submaster switches make partial blackouts of sections of the studio possible. Dimmer controls should be available and installed so they can be patched into individual or submaster switch circuits.

A voice intercom should be incorporated so that the lighting operator can be given directions by the person responsible for the lighting of the performance, if the operator is not directly responsible for it himself. The operator should be positioned with his operating controls in such a way that he can view the entire set as well as a monitor of the telecast.

COAXIAL CABLES

All coaxial cables introduce losses into a system which increase as the frequency of the signal introduced on the coaxial cable is increased. Table 9-2 gives the losses in decibels (db) per 100 feet at frequencies from 1 to 10,000 mc for most types of coaxial cable. Poor or incorrect connector installation can cause additional losses, erratic performance, noise, and interference through coaxial cables. It is imperative that the manufacturer's instructions be followed for removing the outer wrap (usually a durable plastic material), trimming back the braided shield wire, removing the insulation material that separates the braid from the center conductor, and soldering to jacks and plugs. If the wiring is to be done by the plant electrician or the maintenance crew, be certain the staff is given complete training and practice in handling the coaxial cable and its terminations. Once the cables have been drawn through their conduits or laid in their channels (usually in a false ceiling with difficult access) it is extremely time-consuming to attempt to localize suspected sections. The phenomena caused by improperly handled coaxial cables are numerous and elusive; they can seriously limit the usefulness of an entire closed-circuit television system until they are located and repaired.

TALK AND TALLY CIRCUITS

It is advisable to use shield cables (not necessarily coaxial cables) for the low-voltage lines used to actuate tally lights and for audio monitor and intercom signals. The proper use of ground buses and care in making all terminations also assure minimum pickup of unwanted interference that might spoil an otherwise perfect television picture.

Table 9-2. Attenuation of Coaxial Cables

RG/U Cable	Attenuation (db per 100 feet)									
	Frequency (Mc)									
	1	10	50	100	200	400	1,000	3,000	5,000	10,000
5	—	—	—	2.7	4.2	6.2	11.3	22.0	30.0	43.0
5A, 5B	.24	.78	1.8	2.6	3.9	5.5	9.1	17.8	25.0	—
6, 6A	—	—	1.6	2.7	4.2	6.2	11.3	22.0	30.0	43.0
7	.18	.64	1.6	2.4	3.5	5.2	—	—	—	—
8, 8A	.15	.55	1.33	2.0	3.5	4.6	8.0	16.5	27.0	36.0
9	.16	.57	1.38	2.0	2.9	4.25	7.3	15.5	23.0	38.0
9A, 9B	.175	.61	1.47	2.1	3.2	5.0	9.0	18.0	25.0	—
10, 10A	.15	.55	1.33	2.0	3.5	4.6	8.0	16.5	27.0	—
11, 11A, 12, 12A, 13, 13A	.187	.66	1.59	2.3	3.25	4.75	7.8	16.5	26.5	51.0
14, 14A	.12	.41	.98	1.4	2.05	3.1	5.5	12.4	19.0	—
17, 17A, 18, 18A	—	.24	.62	.95	1.5	2.4	4.4	9.5	15.3	—
19, 19A, 20, 20A	—	—	—	.69	1.12	1.85	3.6	7.7	—	—
21, 21A	1.48	4.4	9.3	13.0	18.0	26.0	43.0	85.0	—	—
22	—	—	—	4.6	6.2	8.7	—	—	—	—
22B	—	—	—	3.9	5.6	7.7	12.0	25.0	—	—
29	—	1.2	2.95	4.4	6.5	9.6	16.2	30.0	—	—
34, 34A, 34B	—	—	.85	1.4	2.12	3.28	5.85	16.0	—	—
35, 35A, 35B	—	.235	.58	.85	1.27	1.95	3.5	8.6	15.5	18.0
54, 54A	—	—	—	3.2	4.7	6.8	11.5	25.0	—	—
55, 55A, 55B	—	1.2	3.2	4.8	7.0	10.3	16.7	30.7	46.0	130
57, 57A	—	—	—	—	—	6.0	—	—	—	—
58, 58B	.33	1.25	3.13	4.6	6.9	10.4	17.8	37.5	60.0	—
58A, 58C	—	—	—	6.0	9.0	13.5	24.0	54.0	83.0	247
59, 59A, 59B	.335	1.07	2.4	3.4	4.85	7.0	12.0	26.5	42.0	—
74, 74A	.12	.41	.98	1.4	2.05	3.1	5.5	12.4	19.0	51

Table 9-2. Attenuation of Coaxial Cables (continued)

Attenuation (db per 100 feet)

RG/U Cable	Frequency (Mc)									
	1	10	50	100	200	400	1,000	3,000	5,000	10,000
111, 111A	—	—	—	3.9	5.6	7.7	12.0	25.0	—	—
130, 131	—	—	—	—	—	6.0	—	—	15.5	18.0
164	—	.235	.58	.85	1.27	1.95	3.5	8.6	15.3	—
177	—	.24	.62	.95	1.5	2.4	4.4	9.5	25.0	—
212	.24	.78	1.8	2.6	3.9	5.5	9.1	17.8	27.0	—
213	.15	.55	1.33	2.0	3.5	4.6	8.0	16.5	25.0	38.0
214	.175	.61	1.47	2.1	3.2	5.0	9.0	18.0	27.0	—
215	.15	.55	1.33	2.0	3.5	4.6	8.0	16.5	26.5	—
216	.187	.66	1.59	2.3	3.25	4.7	7.8	16.5	19.0	51.0
217	.12	.41	.98	1.4	2.05	3.1	5.5	12.4	15.3	—
218, 219	—	.24	.62	.95	1.5	2.4	4.4	9.5	—	—
220, 221	—	—	—	.69	1.12	1.85	3.6	7.7	—	—
222	1.48	4.4	9.3	13.0	18.0	26.0	43.0	85.0	—	—
223	—	1.2	3.2	4.8	7.0	10.3	16.7	30.7	46.0	130
224	.12	.41	.98	1.4	2.05	3.1	5.5	12.4	19.0	51.0

Microwave Relays

AT THE BEGINNING of World War II, the development of micro-wave point-to-point equipment reached the stage where it became practical. Since that time, microwaves have been used in thousands of communications systems. They are used to transmit coded data, voice signals, electronic control information, and television images. In some cases, because of terrain or distances to be covered, microwave equipment has been the only feasible means of communication. In other cases, microwave equipment has proven to be more economical than leased cables and telephone lines. Often microwave equipment has been more convenient than any other method of interconnection for two remote points. There is no generality that can be applied when considering the use of microwave point-to-point relay equipment versus coaxial-cable connection. Each situation must be evaluated on the basis of its own peculiar merits, requirements, and variable factors to determine which is more practicable. As the recognition of the capabilities of closed-circuit television grows and as more people and organizations consider the possibilities of an installation, the subject of microwave transmission and reception becomes more frequently discussed.

In answer to growing demands, fixed, mobile, and portable self-contained equipment is being developed and commercially produced. Some transmitters are equipped with coaxial cable input connectors and have input signal requirements which match the electrical outputs of vidicon television cameras. This means that you can simply connect a coaxial cable from the camera to the microwave transmitter and achieve a simple microwave transmission of television pictures. The compatible microwave receiver is fitted with a coaxial cable connector at its output. The characteristics and electrical level of the signal at the coaxial connector of the receiver are such that connection can be made directly to the distribution amplifiers in the closed-circuit television system. Thus, the utility of a closed-circuit television system is extended geographically, providing communications links among places and people that might otherwise be impossible or impractical.

PHENOMENA OF MICROWAVE SIGNALS

The term *microwaves* is generally applied to the spectrum of exceptionally short wavelengths with a frequency of more than 1,000,000,000 cps (1 Gc). In many ways, microwavelength signals behave the same way as a light beam. For example, the range of a microwave signal is limited to the optical or line-of-sight distance between transmitting and receiving antennas. Microwave signals can be either concentrated or focused like a spotlight into a narrow beam path. In addition, much like a spotlight, the beam can be made apparently stronger as a result of this focusing. The beam must be aimed directly and accurately at its target, or it is useless. The same skill is required in setting up the beam radiator of the microwave transmitter as if you were trying to illuminate a distant point with a beam of light. It is essential that the radiator or antenna be aimed directly at the pinpoint target, the receiving antenna. It is equally important that the receiving antenna be pointed directly at the transmitting antenna to achieve optimum results. Even though all factors of equipment operation are optimum, a few degrees deviation from the mutual points-of-aim can result in weak signals or complete lack of signals. It is this requirement for "sharp shooting" that gives microwave communications the characteristics of privacy and lack of interference that are representative of coaxial cables. Thus, a microwave link can be identified as "closed circuit."

Microwaves have none of the limitations inherent in the physical laying of coaxial cables. They can easily hop from roof to roof, span valleys and rivers, or leap from mountain top to mountain top. They can be relayed from transmitter to receiver, retransmitted and relayed over and over again to span continents. Microwave systems can be planned for permanent or temporary installation. For temporary use, a complete antenna and trans-

Courtesy Micro-Link/Lel Corp.

Fig. 10-1. A portable microwave transmitter and receiver.

mitter can be mounted on a tripod, as shown in Fig. 10-1. The transmitter is on the left and the compatible microwave receiver is on the right. The dish-shaped parabolic antennas are an integral part of each unit. The transmitter and receiver are compatible, and mount in the same way. Closeup views of the control panels for both units, located at the back of the units, are shown in Fig. 10-2. (The transmitter is shown at the left and the receiver at the right.) For permanent installations, the microwave equipment and the antenna can be installed in a weatherproof hut or "dog house," as shown in Fig. 10-3.

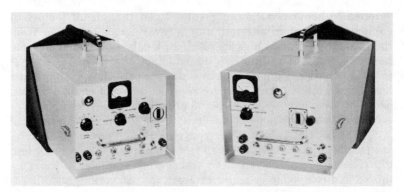

Courtesy Micro-Link/Lel Corp.

Fig. 10-2. Control panels for microwave transmitter and receiver pictured in Fig. 10-1.

Line-of-sight range pertains to all cases illustrated in Figs. 10-3 through 10-6. Therefore the higher the antennas (not the transmitter or receiver), the greater is the distance that can be covered between transmitter and receiver. Generally speaking, the knowledge needed to make a decision regarding the application of microwaves and the choice of equipment has been lacking in many geographic areas. For the most part, this lack of knowledge is due to the fact that relatively few closed-circuit television systems have been sophisticated enough in their requirements to require microwave installations. Consequently, relatively few

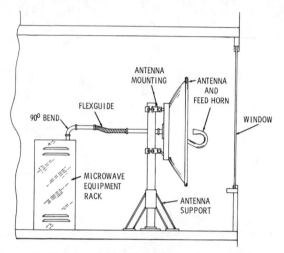

Fig. 10-3. A typical indoor fixed microwave terminal.

people have been in a position to acquire the special knowledge. Microwave equipment, however, is assuming new importance in closed-circuit television systems of all types. In Fig. 10-3 the antenna is aimed through a glass window toward its target. In the fixed installation of Fig. 10-4, the parabolic antenna is mounted directly above the transmitter or receiver on a short supporting column. The short distance between the equipment rack and the antenna is desirable for keeping losses in the interconnecting *flexguide* at minimum. The "radome," a plastic hood, covers the dish-shaped antenna to protect it from weather. In Fig. 10-5 a reflector is located at the top of a tower, and the signal from the antenna is aimed at it. The reflector behaves as a mirror and directs the microwave signals to the terminal at the other end of the shot. Fig. 10-6 shows an installation in which the antenna is at the top of the tower and the transmitting and receiving equipment is below.

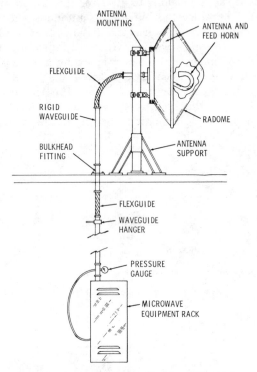

Fig. 10-4. A fixed microwave terminal with roof-mounted antenna.

Unlike intramural closed-circuit, coaxial-cable television systems, microwave equipment and its operations are regulated and licensed by the Federal Communications Commission. The FCC has assigned bands of frequencies specifically for microwave television relays. These bands lie in the 2,000-, 7,000-, and 13,000-mc regions. Because of their greater efficiency and relatively lower equipment costs, many users of microwave equipment prefer to begin their investigations of this medium with equipment designed to operate at the lower frequencies. However, there are many factors that must be taken into account in order to arrive at the optimum arrangement for transmitting and receiving equipment and frequency of operation.

TERRAIN CONSIDERATIONS

The major problems in the designing of any type of microwave link are concerned with the type of path, or profile of the terrain, between the transmitting and receiving points, as well as the distance between the two points. These two factors determine the heights at which the antennas must be located; from this information the tower structures to support the antennas can be planned. It is necessary to determine if there is sufficient "Fresnel-zone" clearance at all points along the path of the microwave transmission. The Fresnel-zone clearance is the minimum height above any object in the path, including tree tops, buildings, and ground elevations.

FRESNEL-ZONE CLEARANCE

For microwave frequencies, reliable communications are directly related to obstructions that must fall below the Fresnel zone. The calculations for determining the needed clearance can be reduced to the following formula.

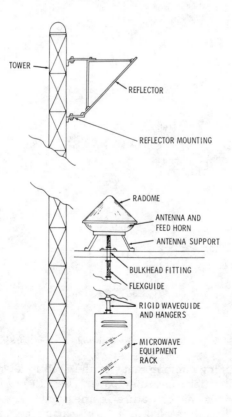

Fig. 10-5. A fixed microwave terminal with parabolic and tower-mounted reflector.

$$H \cong 1316 \sqrt{\frac{AB}{DF}}$$

where,

     H is the minimum clearance in feet,
     A is the distance to obstruction from transmitter,
     B is the distance to obstruction from receiver,
     D is the total distance,
     F is the frequency in megacycles.

In order to determine whether there is a clearance problem, it is necessary to draw a profile of the transmission path. This is

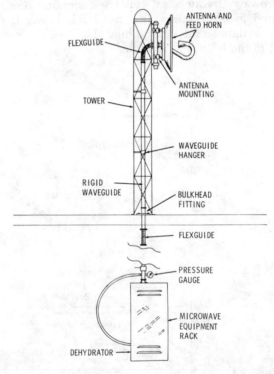

Fig. 10-6. A fixed microwave terminal with tower-mounted antenna.

done by obtaining contour maps of the area involved and transferring the elevations to profile paper (Fig. 10-7), a graph paper which allows for the curvature of the earth. The curvature of the graph is usually scaled at 4/3 the earth's curvature, since a certain amount of refraction is present in the microwave region. This refraction, in effect, reduces the true curvature of the earth.

This graph allows you to draw a straight line, instead of a curved one, from the transmitting to the receiving point. When the profile is drawn, it is a simple matter to determine the heights for the transmitting and receiving antennas to satisfy the requirements for Fresnel-zone clearance.

PARABOLIC ANTENNAS

It was mentioned previously that many of the conditions of a spotlight are analogous to microwave signals. In a spotlight, for example, the light beams are formed into a "spot" by a cone-

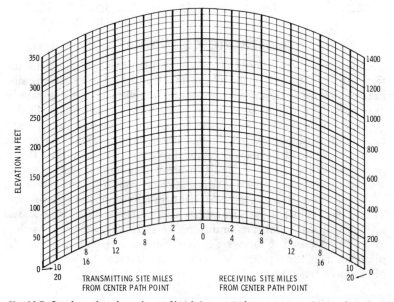

Fig. 10-7. Graph used to draw the profile of the terrain between transmitter and receiver.

shaped lens placed behind the bulb or source of illumination. Microwave signals are formed into a "spot" by a cone-shaped lens, technically called a parabolic antenna and popularly called a "dish." Once the Fresnel-zone clearance conditions are satisfied, the next consideration is the one of signal strength requirements. To determine these requirements, you must add the gains of the elements in the system and subtract the losses. Parabolic antennas have effective gain figures, due to the concentration of energy by the parabolic antenna. As shown in Table 10-1, the gain (in db) of a parabolic antenna varies in accordance with its size, as does its cost.

Table 10-1. Gain of Parabolic Antenna Over Isotropic Radiator

Freq.	ANTENNA DIAMETER, FEET					
mc	2	3	4	6	8	10
900	13	16	19	22	25	27
2000	19.5	23	25.5	29	31.5	33.5
4000	25.5	29	31.5	35	37.5	39.5
6000	29	32.5	35	38.5	41	43
7000	30.5	34	36.5	40	42.5	44.5
10,500	34	37.5	40	43.5	46	48
11,500	35	38	41	44.5	47	49
12,500	35.5	39	41.5	45	47.5	49.5
13,500	36.5	40	42.5	46	48.5	50.5

Courtesy Micro-Link Div., Varian Associates

ATMOSPHERIC CONSIDERATIONS

Losses in a microwave system are due primarily to the attenuation through the atmosphere and the lengths of the transmission line connecting the transmitter and receiver to their parabolic antennas. The gains are due to the parabolic antennas (Table 10-1), and the power gain of the equipment. The end result must be one that allows at least a minimum usable signal to arrive at the input to the receiver. It is important that a safety factor be allowed for those difficult-to-predict instances when signal strength falls due to peculiarities, such as rain, fog, and smog, all of which have the effect of altering the Fresnel-zone clearance. Table 10-2 shows how atmospheric conditions affect the signal strength. Local weather conditions must be taken into consideration in calculating losses so that adequate reliability can be planned into the system to assure satisfactory 1-way or 2-way microwave transmissions.

Table 10-2. Attenuation of Microwaves Due to Weather

Freq.	ATTENUATION PER MILE IN DB						
mc	Mist	Lt. Rain	Mod. Rain	Hvy.	Lt. Snow	Hvy.	Cloudburst
900	0.002	0.004	0.007	0.01	0.002	0.007	0.025
2000	0.007	0.01	0.02	0.03	0.007	0.02	0.085
4000	0.03	0.04	0.09	0.15	0.03	0.09	0.35
6000	0.06	0.09	0.20	0.35	0.06	0.20	0.75
7000	0.09	0.13	0.28	0.45	0.09	0.28	1.05
10,500	0.20	0.28	0.65	1.00	0.20	0.65	2.30
11,500	0.24	0.33	0.75	1.20	0.24	0.75	2.75
12,500	0.28	0.40	0.90	1.40	0.28	0.90	3.20
13,500	0.34	0.47	1.07	1.70	0.34	1.07	3.70

Courtesy Micro-Link Div., Varian Associates

The geographic locations for the transmitter and receiver sites can be taken directly from the maps on which are drawn the profiles of the terrain. Real estate considerations must be taken into account; availability of right-of-ways, power-line facilities, roadways, and other access to the sites are added considerations.

2.5-GC BAND FOR ITV

In 1963 the FCC approved a new channel assignment for fixed-service instructional television. It allows radio interconnection of separate buildings in a school system, primarily for the purpose of the transmission of instructional material. On a secondary basis, the channel may be used for administrative communication purposes and for special training and instruction in safety programs and special skills. Any institutional or governmental organization engaged in the formal education of enrolled students or a nonprofit organization, such as that formed to operate an educational television broadcast station, is eligible to apply for a license. The special channel is within the frequency band of 2.5 Gc to 2.69 Gc. Relay stations may be operated in this band of frequencies to interconnect different systems of the same type but in adjacent geographic areas in order to obtain material from regular television broadcast stations or to deliver instructional material to a closed-circuit system.

Remote-control operation of the station is permitted. At the remote-control position, the operator must be able to turn the transmitter on and off, and he must have a visual indication whenever the transmitting antenna is radiating a signal. A station in this service which is used for relaying the signals of another station, by a translator technique, may be operated unattended.

The power of the transmitter is limited to 10 watts, unless the need is proven for greater power. Directive transmitting antennas must be used where possible, and directive receiving antennas must be used without exception. The emission from the transmitter must be in accordance with the standard television practice with regard to AM visual modulation and FM audio modulation techniques, with the audio carrier 4.5 mc above the visual carrier. Vestigial sideband suppression is not mandatory for the visual signals. No limit is placed on the gain of the transmitting antenna, and any type of polarization may be used.

Transmitters must be type accepted by the FCC. The station operator must hold at least a third-class radiotelephone permit, which requires passing a test to demonstrate knowledge of the FCC regulations, and broad principles of station operation. However, any tests, adjustments or repairs within the transmitter must be done by the holder of at least a second-class radiotelephone license. Call letters are assigned to each transmitter by the FCC. Logs must be maintained. Permission must be obtained prior to any rebroadcast of material originated by a commercial or educational TV station or another fixed instructional station.

This is a highly condensed outline of the FCC regulations for eligibility and service within the so-called 2.5-Gc microwave band. The regulations make the use of microwave equipment as a means of extending the usefulness and capabilities of a closed-circuit television system within a single school district and among adjacent school districts highly feasible. The availability of this channel has resulted in a rapidly growing interest in closed-circuit TV systems and microwave communications at all levels of education.

Circuits and Service

I<small>N STUDYING BLOCK DIAGRAMS</small> and schematics of closed-circuit television cameras and monitors, the TV technician will recognize that there are many similarities to conventional TV sets. This becomes immediately apparent when the block diagram of the VF monitor in Fig. 11-1 is examined. In addition, the technician will notice an amazing likeness in basic principles between closed-circuit TV cameras and conventional home TV sets. This point is illustrated in the block diagram of a VF/RF camera in Fig. 11-2. The basic difference between RF and VF camera block diagrams is the RF modulator, which is omitted on VF-only cameras, and the VF output connector, which is omitted on RF-only cameras. The detail of the block diagram is expanded in Fig. 11-3. When it is recognized that TV cameras and monitors must complement each other's performance, the similarities become less surprising. The camera detects a pattern of light and dark values and converts these values into a series of electrical signals. These signals are distributed to the TV system. The monitor converts the electrical signals into a pattern of light and dark values, as seen on the screen of the picture tube. This is, of course, a highly simplified account of what takes place within the system, but it serves to help emphasize the circuit relationships between a TV camera and monitor.

The controls that are adjusted most frequently are usually labeled with designations familiar to anyone who has ever turned

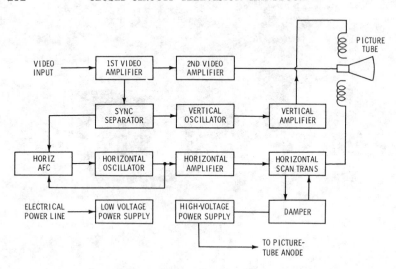

Fig. 11-1. Block diagram of a typical video monitor.

on a TV set, e.g., brightness, contrast, and focus. These are referred to as *primary controls*. It is not at all essential to have a degree in engineering or to have even had prior experience with electronics to adjust the primary controls of a vidicon camera. However, there also are *secondary controls*. In order to adjust these properly, specialized knowledge, or prior experience, is necessary. Although the work can be performed by a TV technician with proper test equipment and the knowledge of how to

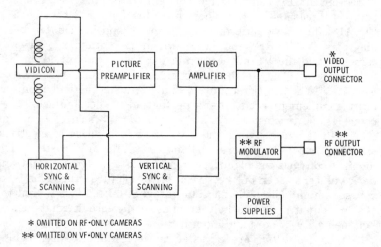

* OMITTED ON RF-ONLY CAMERAS
** OMITTED ON VF-ONLY CAMERAS

Fig. 11-2. A highly simplified block diagram of an RF/VF camera.

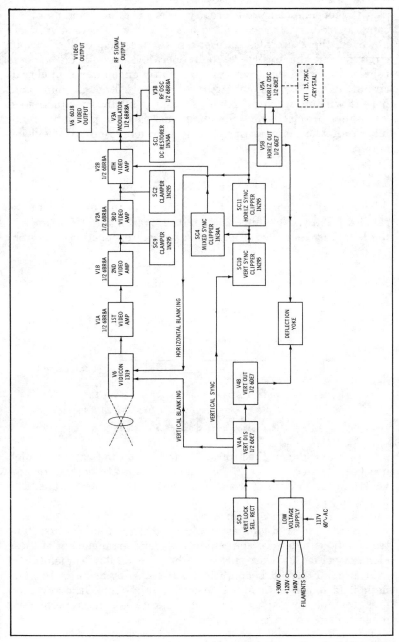

Fig. 11-3. Block diagram of a commercial RF/VF camera.

use it, everyone can profit greatly from an understanding of TV camera circuitry. It was pointed out that there are "similarities"; however, there are also differences. In this chapter the various circuits, and the theory of their operation, of vidicon cameras representative of the type most frequently encountered in closed-circuit television systems will be given. Although maximum benefit will be derived from this chapter by those with a good foundation in electronics fundamentals, there is profitable reading for all who share a responsibility for a closed-circuit television system.

THE VIDICON

The 1-inch vidicon tube is the most popular in closed-circuit TV cameras. The 1-inch dimension is the overall outside diameter; the length is 6⅛ inches. Fig. 11-4 shows a cross-sectional diagram

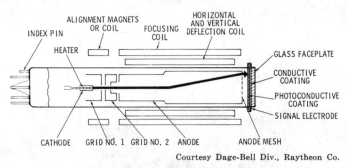

Courtesy Dage-Bell Div., Raytheon Co.

Fig. 11-4. Cross-sectional diagram of a vidicon tube.

of a typical vidicon. Electrons are emitted by the cathode, which has been heated by the heater element, and are accelerated toward the target area at the end as shown by the heavy line. The target area is charged positive with respect to the cathode, attracting the electrons from the cathode. Intermediate elements within the electron-gun assembly accelerate the electron flow from cathode to target. The construction and arrangement of these elements (Fig. 11-5) are such that the electron flow is maintained as a circular-shaped beam. The focus coil provides a fixed magnetic field to concentrate the beam into a fine line. In many cameras the focusing magnetic field is provided by a permanent magnet instead of the focus coil.

The deflection coil also establishes a magnetic field; however, this field is constantly changing. Its purpose is to move the electron beam so that it scans the surface of the target in the same way a picture tube screen of a receiver is scanned. The scanning area of the vidicon is ½ inch wide by ⅜ inch high, a ratio of 4:3. Because of the small area, a small change of current in the vidicon deflection coil is all that is needed to deflect the beam to the extreme edges of the scanning area. When compared with the deflection current in the related coil of a TV set, the average current in the TV camera deflection coil is quite small. It is obvious, therefore, that stray currents and magnetic fields can affect the electron beam, interfering with and distorting the field of scan. For this reason, it is considered good engineering and manufacturing practice to enclose the entire yoke and focus assembly, together with the vidicon tube, in an antimagnetic shield.

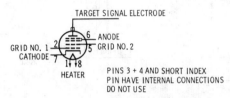

Fig. 11-5. Basing diagram for a vidicon tube.

The mesh screen located at the end of the focus anode has a voltage applied to it. This mesh and the focus anode are out of the field of the deflection coil. The electron flow is decelerated at this point, and the strong attraction on the electron beam exerted by the charged target causes the decelerated electron beam to strike it at a right angle. This assures uniformity of the shape of the electron beam over the entire scanning area, avoiding ovular distortion of the beam. If this type of distortion were allowed, there would be severe loss in the resolution at the corners and edges.

Construction

The target of the vidicon is a layer of photoconductive material deposited on the face of a flat, transparent glass plate. Contact with this material is made by a metal ring built into the outside circumference of the glass plate. A positive voltage (with respect to the cathode) is applied to this ring to provide a uniform charge to the entire surface area of the target. The photoconductive material changes ohmic resistance in an inverse ratio relative to the light that strikes it; that is, the resistance reduces as the light increases.

Light reflected from a scene is optically focused on the target area by the lens system, just as with a motion-picture film camera. The electron beam moves diagonally across the target, scanning

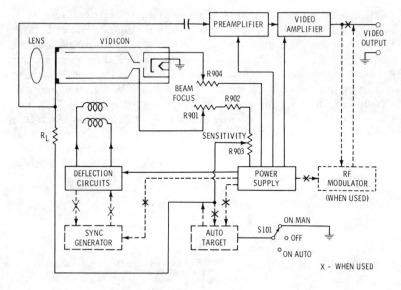

Fig. 11-6. Overall block diagram of a television camera.

the surface. The cathode, electron beam, target, and load resistor R_L in Fig. 11-6 constitute a series circuit through which current flows. As the electron beam strikes a point of light at the target area, the current through the circuit increases. Varying degrees of light intensity cause varying levels of current to flow through the circuit (Fig. 11-7). This increase in current, or this continuously changing current, appears at any given point in the circuit as a voltage change across any of the elements in the series circuit. It is convenient to measure the voltage change across

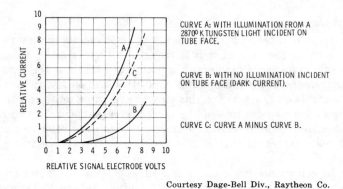

Courtesy Dage-Bell Div., Raytheon Co.

Fig. 11-7. Relative signal energy developed across R_L.

load resistor R_L. Thus, light variations throughout a scene on which the target area is focused through a lens system are converted to voltage variations to produce video information. This is later amplified, combined with synchronizing information, and transmitted to the monitor.

Care of Vidicons

A vidicon is a device of high photosensitivity. It is possible to damage it permanently by pointing it directly at the sun or by aiming it for prolonged periods at an immobile scene with photographic "hot spots." This overloading, or saturation, of the target area makes that target area insensitive to further changes in light. It is possible to "burn" a "hot spot" permanently into the target of the vidicon so that each time the camera is turned on, even if the lens is capped, the burned image will be reproduced as the target is scanned by the electron beam. This type of damage is usually permanent; however, vidicon tubes have been known to recover sufficiently to give adequate performance. It depends, of course, on how much the "ghost" of the burned-in image can be tolerated.

It is recommended that the lens or target area of the vidicon be capped at all times the camera is idle. This practice minimizes the possibility of an accidental burn. Several manufacturers have incorporated a device in their cameras that causes an opaque shutter to fall between the lens and the vidicon automatically when the camera is turned off. This device, however, does not prevent the possibility of burns while the camera is in operation. Only good sense and attention to the scene being illuminated and viewed can provide complete protection. Quite understandably, manufacturers do not warrant against burns that may occur while the vidicon is in the camera or otherwise out of the direct control of the manufacturer.

While storing vidicons, care should be taken that they are not allowed to rest with the target face down. It is possible that extremely small particles of matter may have become dislodged from the tube elements. If these should be allowed to land on and remain on the conductive area of the target, it is probable that pinpoint damage will take place. This can appear as "holes" in the televised picture, and actual and visible dropout of the image caused by interference from the particle with the continuity of the flow of electrons from cathode to target.

The target of the vidicon is heat-sensitive. The temperature of the faceplate should never exceed 71°C (160°F) either in operation or in storage. The optimum temperature for operation and storage ranges between 25°C and 35°C (77°F and 95°F). When it is expected that temperatures at the faceplate will exceed these values, precautions, such as forced-air cooling, must be taken. In addition, from an operational standpoint, maintaining stable temperature conditions reduces the requirement for readjustment of target voltage and assures stability of picture quality.

Image Retention

Persistance of the image can result from the fact that low levels of illumination are being used. This usually causes the operator to advance the brilliance and contrast (beam and target) controls to extreme positions in order to obtain a usable picture. This does not injure the vidicon in any way, but it makes observation of the image difficult as motion of either the image or the camera takes place. Proper illumination of a scene is requisite to good performance of all closed-circuit TV systems. This subject has been discussed in detail in Chapter 9.

Service Standards for Vidicon Spots

For purposes of evaluation of the severity of "spots" or "holes" in the image resulting from particles of impurities that may have fallen on the vidicon target, the monitor screen is divided into two zones, as shown in Fig. 11-8. The inspection procedure is as follows.

1. Using a general-purpose lens, all controls on the camera are adjusted for the best picture as seen on a 17-inch monitor.
2. Place a white card in front of the lens. The card should have a uniformly white surface. Do not stop down the lens or make other adjustments to either the monitor or the camera.

ZONE 1 IS THE AREA COVERED BY A CENTRALLY POSITIONED CIRCLE, THE DIAMETER OF WHICH IS EQUAL TO THE MONITOR SCREEN HEIGHT

ZONE 2 REPRESENTS THE TWO SIDE AREAS COMPRISING THE REMAINDER OF THE MONITOR SCREEN

Courtesy Sylvania Electric Products, Inc.

Fig. 11-8. Standard for determining vidicon quality with reference to spots.

3. In Zone 1 (Fig. 11-8), any number of spots or holes up to 3/32 inch maximum dimension are allowed. In addition, not more than three spots over 3/32 inch but not larger than 5/32 inch are allowed. No spots over 5/32 inch are allowed.

4. In Zone 2 any number of spots measuring 5/32 inch or under are allowed. No spots over 5/32 inch are allowed.

Notes:

(a) Spots will normally be seen as two or three spots joined together. Measurement should only be made on a single spot, and not the group.

(b) The spot to be measured should be that having the greatest contrast or visibility. It may be either black or white.

(c) Spots will usually have the greatest visibility when no light is allowed to enter the camera lens.

(d) Spots should be evaluated subjectively as well as by the dimensions given in Points 1 through 4. It is possible to have a large number of spots and still be within limits. If these spots are of high brilliance or visibility, however, the vidicon should be rejected.

(e) If a vidicon has more than three spots in Zone 1 measuring over 3/32 inch, but not over 5/32 inch, it is outside the limit as in Point 3. However, if these spots are of low visibility, they are not cause for rejection.

(f) A spot larger than 5/32 inch but located near the edge of the monitor screen would not necessarily be cause for vidicon rejection.

(g) Some vidicons will have one or more irregularly shaped dots, spots, or areas which are larger than 5/32 inch. These are considered *blemishes*. The evaluation of their efforts on performance would have to be subjective to determine acceptance or rejection.

SYNCHRONIZATION

The primary functions of the camera and monitor are to "photograph" and reproduce a photo image. The vidicon tube in the camera has an electron beam that scans the target area; the picture tube in the monitor has an electron beam that scans the phosphor-coated screen. The scanning motions of both beams are controlled by horizontal and vertical circuit elements that generate electrical pulses. It is essential that both beams be synchronized, each starting at the same point, at the same instant.

A secondary function of the camera is to generate, or provide, the electrical pulses that synchronize the vidicon and picture-tube electron beams. Therefore, in addition to picture signals, the TV camera must transmit "sync" information that can be used by the monitor. The sync signal generator is often an integral part of the camera circuitry. The characteristics of sync signals are standardized by industry agreement. They are so specified as to enable compatibility from equipment to equipment regardless of make or model. Cameras (and monitors) that have integrated sync generators can be adjusted manually to bring the cameras and monitors into sync with each other. The controls for this manual adjustment are the familiar "vertical hold" and "horizontal hold." Commercial television stations broadcast signals that contain the sync information as a reference for the TV set. Because of the aforementioned standardization, as well as FCC regulations, you can switch from TV channel to TV channel without having to readjust the hold controls.

In the simplest closed-circuit television system, with only one camera and one monitor, the standards are of relatively little importance. If enough latitude in adjustment is provided by the hold controls, one unit can be adjusted to sync with the other. However, the moment more than a single unit of equipment of the same category is introduced into the system, a standard must be developed as a point of reference. In practice, when more than one monitor is used with a single camera, the camera conveniently becomes the "reference." The hold controls on the monitor are adjusted to sync with the camera. It should be pointed out that when a picture is out of sync, the visual indication is vertical roll or horizontal jitters. When all monitors are in sync with the reference camera, you can switch from monitor to monitor without losing sync. The introduction of a second camera to the system introduces a potential sync problem. One of the two cameras must be established as the standard against which the monitors are adjusted for hold. The second camera, then, is adjusted for hold with the monitors as the reference.

THE SCANNING BEAM

The camera-tube beam scans, or sweeps, the viewed scene line by line, starting at the top and ending at the bottom of the target area. It is standard that one complete television "frame" has 525 horizontal lines. In both the camera and the monitor, each line is scanned at a uniform rate. When the electron beam reaches the end of the line, it switches rapidly back to begin the next line, repeating this process until this particular frame is ended. This quick return of the scanning beam to begin the next line is called the retrace period. During retrace, the beam must be "blanked" or you would see it return each time to begin another line or frame. This retrace period must be a "dark" interval. Essentially the beam is turned off at both the camera and the monitor during retrace.

The scanning system just described produces a synchronized picture on a TV screen, but unless it is very rapid, the screen will "flicker." In order to simulate motion and to prevent flicker, a modified scanning method is sometimes used. This is called *interlace* scanning.

Interlace Scanning

In interlace scanning, the electron beam scans the image, as previously described, but the horizontal lines are divided into two "fields." The first field consists of the odd-numbered lines and the second field consists of the even-numbered lines. Since there is a total of 525 lines per frame, each field has 262½ lines. In order to get the ½ lines in, the scanning is started at the middle of the top line in one field and ends at the middle of the bottom line on the other field.

For each complete picture, 525 lines are scanned to become a complete frame. The frame is repeated 30 times each second. The retentive sense of the human eye is such that the frames appear as a continuous scene. Since 30 frames are scanned per second and each frame consists of 525 lines or cycles of beam travel, the horizontal scanning frequency is 15,750 cycles per second (525 × 30). Two fields (one frame) are scanned for each frame, and there are 30 frames each second. It follows that the vertical scanning frequency is 60 cycles per second. It is convenient, therefore, where the power lines are at 60 cycles per second, to use the power line as the reference for the vertical-scanning generator at both the camera and the monitor.

Sawtooth-shaped pulses are generated to move the scanning beam in the horizontal and vertical directions. To interlock the horizontal and vertical pulses so that they occur at the correct time, the sawtooth generators are triggered by synchronizing pulses. This system is known as 2:1 interlace scanning.

Random Scanning

The same quality of picture, with some exceptions, can be achieved with a technique known as random, sequential, or free-running scanning. When horizontal triggering pulses are developed in a free-running multivibrator (oscillator) and the vertical pulses are derived from the 60-cycles-per-second power lines, there is no positive interlock. The differences in frequency between the oscillator and the power line may cause a slight drift over a period of time. However, this drift may be so slight that the human eye cannot always discern it. When it is discernible, a slight readjustment of hold controls corrects the picture disturbance.

Random interlace is inexpensive, and it is adequate where high vertical resolution is not a performance requirement. It is used by virtually all home entertainment-type TV sets, as well as by economy-priced TV cameras.

The signal output of the camera picture pickup tube is measured in microvolts. It is preamplified and amplified before it is fed via coaxial cable to the distribution system. The output signal from the camera contains the elements of the viewed scene and the horizontal and vertical synchronizing pulses that keep the monitor screens in step with the picture pickup tube beam. In addition, it serves to turn the monitor beam off when the camera beam is blanked. The strength of the monitor scanning beam is controlled by the amplitude of the incoming video signal, which varies in accordance with the light and dark areas of the scene being viewed by the camera.

Frequency-Stabilizing Sync Generators

As more cameras and monitors are added to the closed-circuit television system the interlocking of the synchronizing generators for all units becomes more complex. When sync has been lost in a free-running system, you can become thoroughly confused trying to determine whether the camera or the monitor needs adjustment to restore normal operation. Such a situation can develop as the frequency of oscillation drifts or shifts. This drift is especially pronounced during the initial warmup period of tube-type cameras and monitors which require some time, often hours, to stabilize after the power has been applied from a cold start. The aging of tubes and components can also introduce frequency drift or shift in a free-running sync system. A crystal-controlled horizontal-oscillator circuit will increase the frequency stability. Such a circuit is recommended where more than one camera is used in a system or where the camera in a one-camera installation is not readily accessible for adjustment. The crystal is ground by the manufacturer for 15,750-cps operation and enclosed in a hermetically sealed can. It will not drift significantly in frequency under normal conditions of ambient temperature.

External Sync Generators

Commercial broadcasters use numerous cameras and monitors during a single day's broadcast. Several cameras may be used during a single program. At the director's signal, each is selected to provide different angles, closeups, and long shots to enhance the overall production. A large number of monitors are also used. They are located in the control room, on the studio floor, and throughout the station facilities. Imagine the enormous task of trying to synchronize all the monitors and cameras if each had its own integral sync generator with its individual controls. In addition, in such a system, there would be a large duplication of circuitry, and manpower and equipment efficiencies would be very low and dissipated in repetition and redundance.

It is common practice, therefore, in commercial TV, and in closed-circuit TV systems where large numbers of monitors and cameras are used, to provide a single sync generator for the entire system. The horizontal, vertical, and blanking signals are generated by a master unit. These signals are "piped" throughout the facility. Cameras and monitors "plug-in" to derive their AC power, sync information, and all electrical interconnections. Thus, each camera and monitor is automatically locked or held in synchronism with all other units connected to the system sync generator. Any drift or shift in the generator will simultaneously affect all cameras and monitors in the system; there will be no apparent change in the viewed picture.

In an open-circuit or commercial-TV broadcast station, a drift in the frequency of the master sync generator would tend to cause, if the drift were appreciable, pictures on the TV sets tuned to that channel to roll or scramble. The viewer would then have to readjust the hold controls of his TV set. However, generators used in commercial-TV broadcasting as master sync-signal sources are designed and maintained to provide exceptionally high reliability of the transmitted reference signals. Of course, closed-circuit television systems using master sync generators achieve the same advantage in stability of pictures from camera to camera and monitor to monitor.

THE VIDEO AMPLIFIER

An amplifier for the voltage changes that appear across the target load resistor (R_L in Fig. 11-6) is located immediately following the vidicon in a camera block diagram. This is the *video* amplifier. Resolution is related to bandwidth. It is requisite, therefore, that the video amplifier be capable of passing and

Courtesy Dage-Bell Div., Raytheon Co.

Fig. 11-9. The Dage Model 320B closed-circuit television camera with electronic viewfinder.

amplifying a broad band of frequencies. It must be designed and maintained in its adjustments to ensure the maximum resolution capability of the camera. A typical bandwidth is 8 mc for a 600-line resolution. That bandwidth must pertain to the overall performance of the system, not to the camera alone. The narrower the bandwidth, the lower is the achieved resolution. You can expect approximately 100 lines of horizontal resolution at the center of the monitor screen for every 1.3 mc of system bandwidth. To estimate bandwidth requirements in megacycles to achieve a specific number of lines of resolution, multiply the number of lines by 0.013. To estimate the number of horizontal lines from a known bandwidth, divide the bandwidth in megacycles by 1.3.

TYPICAL TUBE-TYPE CAMERA

As a practical example of tube-type camera circuits, we shall refer to the Dage Model 320B camera. Figs. 11-9 and 11-10 show the camera and its electronic viewfinder completely assembled for operation. The location of significant sections is given in Fig. 11-11. Referring to the block diagram of the video preamplifier section (Fig. 11-12), you can trace the signal from the output of the vidicon. The signal is coupled to the parallel-connected grids of V401, a dual-triode preamplifier stage. The triode is paralleled in order to have high current capabilities with low noise. This is the input section of a cascode-connected amplifier designed to provide high gain consistent with low noise. V101 is the second, or output, half of the cascode circuit. It provides a heavy current load on the input section which results in excellent stability. The Miller effect (increase of input capacity with an increase in gain) is reduced. This improves the high-frequency response characteristics. Series and shunt peaking coils compensate for high frequencies; resistors shunted across these peaking coils broaden their response.

Courtesy Dage-Bell Div., Raytheon Co.

Fig. 11-10. The camera in Fig. 11-9 with the side panels opened.

Because the response of the vidicon falls off at high frequencies, it is necessary to have good high-frequency response, with compensation in the preamplifier stages, in order to achieve good picture shading. The means used to achieve this effectively "flat" response characteristic must do so with minimum phase shift to prevent smearing of the vertical edges. V102A provides the necessary phase correction in the Dage Model 320B camera. Part of the high-frequency loss in the vidicon is due to the fact that the scanning spot, or aperture, is not dimensionless. The correction for high frequencies, therefore, is termed *aperture correction*. Perfect reproduction would require an instantaneous change in voltage as the beam is moved from one picture scene element to another. This is impossible to obtain in any pickup tube. The aperture must logically be on both scene elements

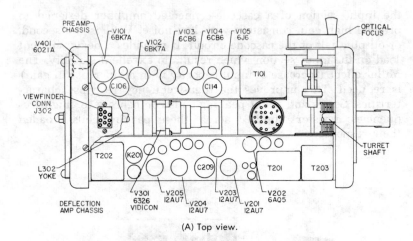

(A) Top view.

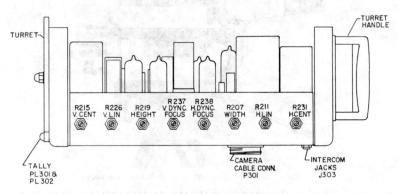

(B) Deflection amplifier chassis.

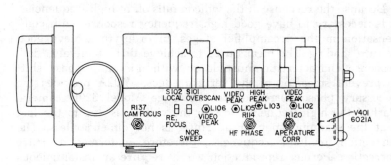

(C) Preamplifier chassis.

Courtesy Dage-Bell Div., Raytheon Co.

Fig. 11-11. Component layout for the Dage Model 320B camera.

simultaneously for a specific length of time during its transition. This time is dependent on the spot size and the speed of the beam. The transition time is analogous to the square-wave response of the video amplifier.

Aperture correction necessarily causes phase shift at high frequencies. Phase corrector V102A compensates for this phase shift. Referring to Fig. 11-13 it can be seen that C109 is large enough to pass almost all frequencies appearing at the output of V102A to the grid of V102B. At the same time, C108 passes only high frequencies from the cathode of V102A. This, too, is coupled to the

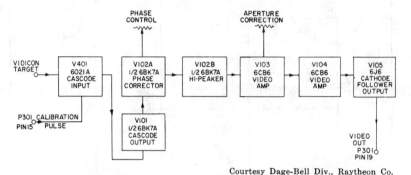

Courtesy Dage-Bell Div., Raytheon Co.

Fig. 11-12. Block diagram of the video preamplifier chassis.

grid of V102B. Adjustment of R114 determines the amount of, or balance of, all frequencies fed to the grid of V102B. R114, therefore, selects the phase of the high-frequency component.

V102B is a high-frequency peaking stage, and V103 (Fig. 11-12) is a video amplifier with shunt and series peaking in the plate circuit. V104 also is a video amplifier with a peaking control in the cathode for aperture correction. Shunt and series peaking is also provided in the plate circuit of V104. The signal output of V104 is fed to a cathode-follower output (V105) which has a high current gain to match the video amplifier to a low-impedance load, such as a coaxial cable.

Beam Deflection and Blanking

A multivibrator in the camera control section of Dage Model 320B supplies controlled width pulses to the grid of V204A (Fig. 11-14). These pulses are amplified by V204A and fed to vertical discharge tube V204B. In the absence of these pulses, V204B is cut off. During the cutoff period, a capacitor is charged to a potential determined by the setting of the height control. The positive-going excursions of the charge at the capacitor are

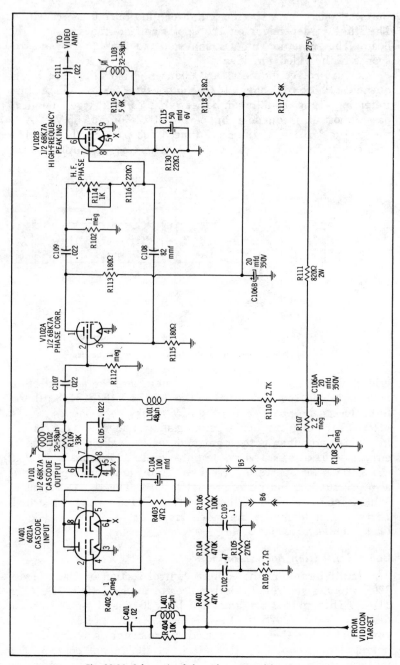

Fig. 11-13. Schematic of the video preamplifier chassis.

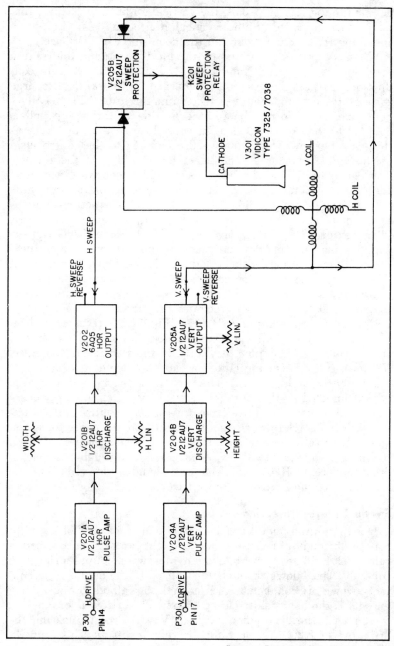

Courtesy Dage-Bell Div., Raytheon Co.

Fig. 11-14. Block diagram of the deflection amplifier stages.

coupled to the grid of V205A, the vertical output tube. This signal is, in turn, coupled to the vertical deflection coils through a matching transformer to sweep the beam for vertical trace.

When the pulses generated by the multivibrator in the camera control unit are present at V204B, the tube is driven into conduction, causing the previously charged capacitor to discharge through the low impedance of the conducting tube. This negative-going excursion forms the retrace portion of the sweep and is coupled to the vertical deflection coils through the same path as the trace portion. This signal is also coupled to the control grid of the vidicon to cut off the beam for blanking of the retrace. The capacitor then recharges to form the sweep for trace time. Linearity is controlled by varying the bias on output tube V205A. The height and linearity controls are interactive—the adjustment of one usually requires the readjustment of the other.

The external power supply for the Dage Model 320B camera supplies bias to position the scan on the vidicon. The vertical centering control varies the amount and direction of the current flow through the deflection coils. When reversed sweep is used, a switch reverses the output transformer connections and inserts the required components to recenter the picture.

Horizontal pulse amplifier V201A (Fig. 11-14) receives a negative pulse of controlled width from the control unit of the camera. It is amplified and coupled to V201B. In the absence of this pulse, V201B is cut off. During cutoff, a capacitor is charged as determined by the width control. The process of charge and discharge is very much like that for the vertical sweep circuit previously described. When the pulse from the camera control unit is impressed on V201B, it is driven into conduction, the capacitor is discharged, and the retrace portion of the sweep is formed. Vidicon blanking is applied to the vidicon cathode through contacts of protection relay K201. The blanking signal is derived from the secondary of the horizontal output transformer.

Sweep Failure Protection

During normal operation, the cathode current path of the vidicon is through a resistor and through contacts of protection relay K201. Plate current through the sweep failure protection tube (V205B) flows through the coil of K201, holding the contacts, which are connected in series with the cathode of the vidicon and its cathode resistor, closed. If either horizontal or vertical sweep fails, the conduction through V205B drops, releasing the armature of K201 and opening the relay contacts. This immediately turns off the electron beam and prevents a spot from being burned into the target by the stationary beam.

The Electronic Viewfinder

The viewfinder enables the operator to properly frame the scene, select the correct lens, and monitor the output quality of the camera. The viewfinder is usually mounted atop the camera; however, in some closed-circuit television systems a completely separate, conventional monitor is employed. This monitor must be positioned so that the cameraman can view it while maneuvering the camera.

The Dage Model 320A electronic viewfinder is a companion to the 320B camera. It is completely self contained and capable of being mounted in its own housing directly on top of the camera (Fig. 11-10). The picture is displayed on the face of a 5AYP4 cathode-ray tube. Electromagnetic deflection and electrostatic deflection are used. Referring to Figs. 11-15 and 11-16, the incoming video signal is amplified by V101, a conventional video amplifier, and is coupled to V102, the video output tube. The output tube has an adjustment for peaking high-frequency response. The video signal is then applied to the CRT in negative-black polarity. When the brightness control is properly set, the signal swings the CRT into cutoff for blacks and allows it to conduct for whites and intermediate shades of gray. The same pulses which are applied to the vertical and horizontal sections of the camera are utilized to develop sweep voltages in the viewfinder.

The viewfinder uses an RF power supply for high voltage and for the focus voltage for the picture tube. The RF oscillator is a Hartley type, feeding its signal to a voltage doubler for the picture-tube anode voltage and to a single rectifier for the focus voltage. The picture-tube cathode receives an additional blanking voltage from the plate of V103A which allows the use of a bright raster without displaying vertical retrace lines.

Tally Light and Intercom

The tally light and intercom facilities require power from a source other than the camera. That source should be the switcher used in conjunction with the system. Thus, when a push button on the switcher is depressed to select a particular camera in the chain, the tally light for the selected camera will be lighted. Communication circuits in the Model 320B are relayed through the camera control units. An induction coil in the camera provides connection for the mike and headset worn by the camera operator.

Primary Controls

The primary controls for focus, target, and beam may be incorporated in the camera unit but are usually installed in the

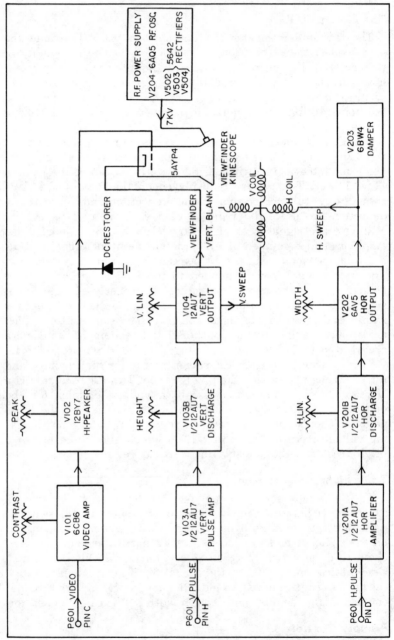

Courtesy Dage-Bell Div., Raytheon Co.

Fig. 11-15. Block diagram of the electronic viewfinder.

master control room. They are adjusted by the console operator at that point. The relationship between the target and beam controls is critical for optimum picture. The target control affects shading and contrast of the picture for a given amount of scene

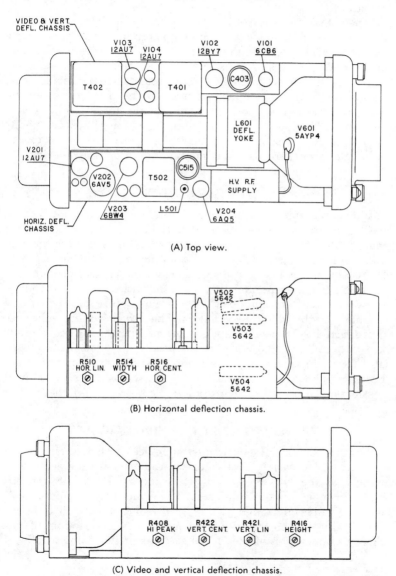

(A) Top view.

(B) Horizontal deflection chassis.

(C) Video and vertical deflection chassis.

Courtesy Dage-Bell Div., Raytheon Co.

Fig. 11-16. Component layout for the electronic viewfinder.

illumination. If low light levels are encountered, the target control may be used to increase sensitivity of the vidicon tube. The target voltage is limited only by the amount of dark current encountered. High target voltage increases the tendency to "image retention."

When the beam control is at maximum (maximum grid bias), the beam is completely cut off and no picture appears. Turning the beam control to decrease the vidicon grid bias results in resolution of the dark portions of the scene. Further rotation gradually resolves the brightest highlights. This results from the fact that only a small amount of beam current is needed to resolve the darker portions (less positive points on the target), but such a current will not resolve the brighter areas (more positive points on the target). As the beam current is increased to an excess value, the beam spreads and resolution of the picture deteriorates.

VIDEO MONITORS

Video monitors are the same in theory of operation as the electronic viewfinder—with certain modifications in individual makes. Monitors may have internal generators for synchronizing and blanking pulses, or they may, as in the case of the Dage Model 320A viewfinder, take these signals from the camera control unit or from a master generator that feeds the entire system. Of course, video monitors are equipped with larger picture tubes than are normally required for viewfinders. The larger picture tubes require that larger power supplies be incorporated. Such circuits are quite conventional; they are essentially the same as those used in TV sets for home entertainment. Transistorized monitors are becoming popular because of their light weight and reduced heat dissipation; especially when used as electronic viewfinders.

TRANSISTORIZED CAMERA CIRCUITS

The application of semiconductor devices to closed-circuit TV cameras is increasing. Transistorized cameras use the same type vidicon as the tube or hybrid-type cameras. The associated circuits, however, are quite different. The Cohu/KinTel Model 20/20 is an example of a high-quality transistorized camera designed specifically for closed-circuit television. A description of the theory of operation of individual sections of this camera follows.

Deflection

The deflection and blanking subassembly generates, shapes, and amplifies the vertical and horizontal waveforms that control the sequence of operation of the entire system. Four major signals are formed by this subassembly: composite blanking (vertical and horizontal); camera blanking (vidicon protect); horizontal drive, and vertical drive. A portion of the horizontal sweep pulse is made available to the video amplifier for use as a video clamping pulse. The deflection circuits (Fig. 11-17) are designed for use with both sequential (random or free-running) and 2:1 interlace scan. To obtain 2:1 interlace scan it is necessary to install a sync-generator accessory subassembly.

Vertical Oscillator—The vertical oscillator (Fig. 11-18) is essentially a blocking oscillator that generates the 60-cps vertical deflection pulses. The basic frequency of oscillation is set by the applied bias voltage. When the line lock is jumpered (Fig. 11-18), sequential scan (random interlace) is used. When a sync-generator accessory is used, the line-lock jumper is removed, and the oscillator is synchronized to the vertical pulses from the sync generator. The frequency of the oscillator is adjustable (within limits) by potentiometer R103. The vertical drive pulses generated in the oscillator are applied simultaneously to an NPN transistor switch and to a pulse-stretcher diode (CR103).

The vertical pulse present across the collector load resistor (R105 in Fig. 11-18) is applied to stretching diode CR103. The bias for this diode is set by R107. When the diode conducts, C104 charges rapidly and discharges slowly. This action sets the width of the vertical pulses applied to the shaper/clipper stage. "Stretching" enables system blanking to end after camera blanking.

A transistor, operated as a shaper/clipper stage between the blocking oscillator and the blanking mixer, serves to isolate the blocking oscillator and amplifies the pulse slightly before applying it to the vertical blanking mixer.

The presence of the vertical drive pulse in the base circuit of the NPN switch transistor turns it on. Conduction is for the period of the pulse. Phase inversion is also achieved in this stage. A delay network in this stage retards the vertical sweep slightly so that system blanking starts before vertical retrace.

Sawtooth Generator—Capacitors C109 and C110 in the sawtooth generator circuit of Fig. 11-19 are connected in series to the power source (−20 volts). The capacitors charge during the nonconductive periods of transistor Q104. When a pulse is present at the base of Q104, the transistor conducts, thus shorting C109 and C110 to ground. This discharges the capacitors and initiates the retrace time. The sawtooth output is applied to Q105, the vertical output stage, through coupling capacitor C111.

Vertical Amplifier and Output—The vertical drive sawtooth pulse formed by the discharge of C109 (Fig. 11-19) and C110

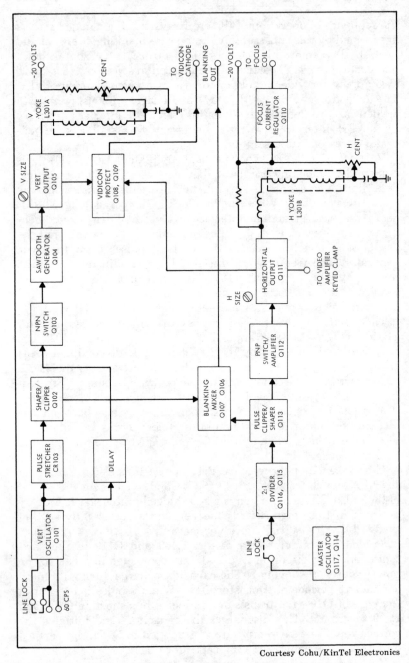

Courtesy Cohu/KinTel Electronics

Fig. 11-17. Transistorized TV camera deflection circuits.

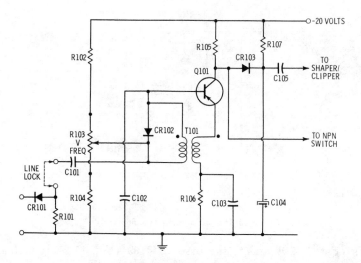

Fig. 11-18. Simplified schematic of the vertical oscillator.

during the conduction time of Q104 is applied to transistor Q105. This stage operates as a Class-A amplifier with feedback through R115, a current-limiting resistor. Current feedback aids in making the sawtooth linear.

Potentiometer R119 in the emitter circuit of Q105 (Fig. 11-19) controls the amplification of the stage; thus, it is the vertical size control. The vertical output is applied to the vertical deflection

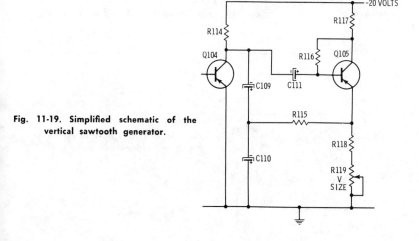

Fig. 11-19. Simplified schematic of the vertical sawtooth generator.

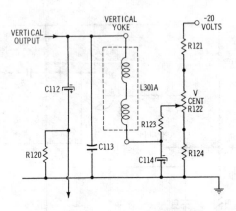

Fig. 11-20. The vertical output configuration.

coils (Fig. 11-20) and to the base of Q109 (Fig. 11-21), which is one of the transistors in the vidicon protection circuit. Potentiometer R122 (Fig. 11-20) is part of a balanced voltage-divider circuit and is the vertical centering control. This control adjusts the DC base of the vertical deflection coils.

Vidicon Protection Circuit—Failure of either the vertical or horizontal scanning signals would cause the electron beam to become fixed. If the beam is allowed to remain in one spot for any length of time, an unrepairable spot can be burned into the target. To prevent this, Q108 and Q109 in Fig. 11-21 operate as a special type of AND gate; they sample the horizontal and vertical output as they appear across their respective yoke coils. The two transistors are biased so they normally conduct. In the presence of

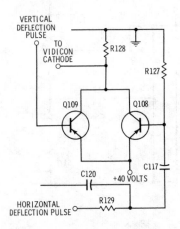

Fig. 11-21. Schematic of the vidicon
protection circuit.

deflection signals, however, they become nonconducting. The emitters of both transistors are connected directly to the +40 volt bus. In the absence of either deflection signal, the collectors go from zero to +40 volts; this voltage appears across common collector load resistor R128. The vidicon cathode is connected to the collectors of Q108 and Q109. The +40 volts effectively cuts off the vidicon beam until sync signals are restored. During retrace time, deflection signals are absent, the beam cut off, and blanking results.

The Horizontal Oscillator—The master oscillator is crystal controlled at 31.5 kc for 525-line scan. For 729-line scan, a 43.74-kc crystal is used. When a sync-generator accessory board is used, connections are made to "slave" the sync generator to the crystal oscillator. During random (free-running) interlace, the oscillator output is connected to a flip-flop stage which divides the oscillator frequency by two to arrive at the horizontal line scan frequency of 15,750 cps (21,870 cps for fine-line operation).

A simplified diagram of the familiar flip-flop circuit is given at Fig. 11-22. A pair of "steering" diodes (CR1 and CR2) has been added. The flip-flop has two stable states. At the moment the camera is turned on, the flip-flop automatically falls into one of its two stable states. Assume Q1 is off; its collector, therefore, will be at high potential. Q2 is then forward-biased and conducts heavily. Under these conditions, crystal diode CR1 will be back-biased more than CR2, effectively holding the flip-flop in its present state.

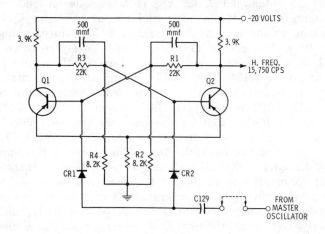

Fig. 11-22. Simplified schematic of the flip-flop circuit used to generate the horizontal pulses.

A positive input pulse will cause the diode, which is less back-biased (CR2 in this case), to conduct and "steer" the pulse. The pulse raises the base potential of Q2 in the positive direction, effectively cutting the transistor off and causing the flip-flop to change state. Now CR2 is more back-biased than CR1, and the next incoming input pulse causes the flip-flop to return to its original state. Since the output is taken from one side of the flip-flop, a frequency division by two has taken place, and the horizontal frequency of 15,750 cps or 21,870 cps is achieved.

The horizontal pulses are fed to a pulse clipper/shaper transistor in a grounded-emitter amplifier circuit. This circuit is designed to conduct for a short time at the leading edge of the incoming pulse. The resultant constant-amplitude clipper pulse of very short duration is applied to an NPN-transistor switch and to the blanking mixer.

Since a transistor will function as a very good switch, i.e., has a very low resistance when "on" and a high resistance when "off," a simple and reliable horizontal sweep pulse is obtained in the switching stage. The switching transistor is operated as a grounded-emitter circuit and conducts heavily when a pulse appears in its base circuit. Its output is coupled to the horizontal output stage.

Horizontal Output—The horizontal output stage uses a single transistor operating as a low-dissipation on-off switch to circulate energy among the various reactive elements. Low power consumption and the transient difficulties that give rise to ringing are substantially eliminated. L102 (Fig. 11-23), a collector load choke, is a ringing device. When horizontal output transistor Q111 is cut off, the collapsing magnetic field of L102 induces a higher peak voltage than can be obtained from a purely resistive collector load; therefore a larger horizontal drive pulse is obtained.

Potentiometer R134 (Fig. 11-23) controls the horizontal size by varying the collector voltage of horizontal-sweep output transistor Q111. C122 is a bypass filter capacitor. When Q111 is turned off by the horizontal pulse from the previous stage, the collector current of the output stage "rings" in inductor L102. The first "ring" excursion is the horizontal pulse which is applied to the yoke. CR105 clips off and damps the succeeding rings. The pulse of voltage is then applied to the horizontal deflection coils, where a sawtooth signal is generated. Since this coil has some resistance, the sweep current will rise exponentially, instead of linearly. To increase the total Q of the circuit and make current more linear, a high-Q toroidal coil, L101, is connected in series with the horizontal deflection coils.

Potentiometer R133 in Fig. 11-23 adjusts the DC base of the horizontal deflection coils. Essentially, it varies the current through the coils to affect the centering. A portion of the horizontal drive pulse from the collector of the horizontal output stage is made available to the video amplifier. Its purpose is to clear hum and noise from the signal and provide a DC (black) reference level. This pulse is applied during flyback to clamp the black (when the vidicon has been turned off).

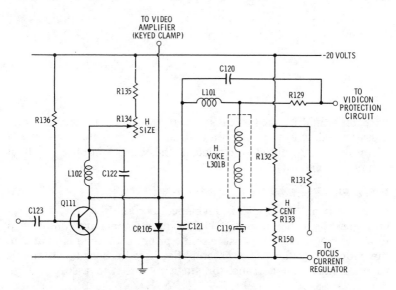

Fig. 11-23. Schematic of the horizontal output amplifier.

Focus Coil Current Regulator

The magnetic focus field for the vidicon is generated by a current that must be held extremely constant since a small variation has a marked effect on the picture focus. The current through the focus coil is maintained constant by the simplified circuit shown in Fig. 11-24. Zener diode CR104 provides a regulated fixed bias for the base of transistor Q110, and it maintains constant current through the transistor and the series-connected focus coil.

Blanking Mixer

The blanking mixer consists of two transistors operated as a mixer pair (basically an OR gate) with a common collector load resistor. The horizontal pulse is applied to the base of one transistor from the pulse clipper/shaper. The vertical pulse is applied to the base of the second transistor. Appearance of a pulse in the

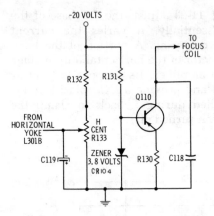

Fig. 11-24. The focus current-regulator circuit.

base of either transistor causes that transistor to conduct and current to flow in the common collector load resistor. The output of the blanking mixer is applied to the video amplifier to effect composite blanking.

Video Preamplifier

The vidicon signals are developed across R801 in the preamplifier stage shown in Fig. 11-25. These signals are conditioned in a flat frequency response circuit, prior to their application to the video amplifier. The preamplifier circuit board contains a vacuum tube and a transistor stage in order to assure a high

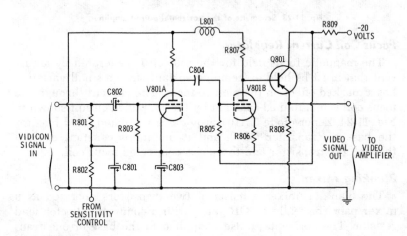

Fig. 11-25. The video preamplifier stage.

signal-to-noise ratio. Dual-triode V801 is operated as a cascode-connected low-voltage amplifier coupled to a transistor output stage. The input impedance is high to match the output impedance of the vidicon load resistor. The output impedance of the stage is low. Thus, the circuit acts as an impedance-matching transformer between the vidicon and the video amplifier, in addition to providing amplification of the vidicon signal.

Sync Generator

Reference was made to an accessory "sync-generator" board that could be installed to achieve 2:1 interlace scan. The circuitry for such a generator is quite interesting; because it is reasonable to expect that such generators will become more in demand, it is worthwhile to devote some attention to this type unit.

The block diagram for the sync generator is given in Fig. 11-26. The output of the crystal oscillator on the deflection circuit board is applied to the master oscillator of the sync-generator board. A series of flip-flop multivibrator binary counters divides the output frequency of the master oscillator, with appropriate feedback at predetermined points, to produce the vertical scan synchronizing signal of 60 cps. Automatic frequency control corrects phase difference between the AC line and the vertical output.

After acquisition of the crystal oscillator output frequency, the generation of sync pulses is essentially a series of switching operations. As transistors are particularly well suited to switching functions, the sync generator is completely transistorized.

The master oscillator (Q212) is a conventional Colpitts-type oscillator. The tuned circuit is common to both the input and output. The slug-tuned inductance in the tuned circuit adjusts the oscillator frequency. The voltage applied to the base of the oscillator transistor is a combination of negative DC dropped from the −20-volt bus and the phase detector circuit. Thus, the base voltage varies, depending on the relationship between the 60-cycle vertical output and the 60-cps power line.

The signal from the phase detector is applied to the base of transistor Q213, the reactance stage. The signal of either polarity thus varies the base bias of the stage. This effectively varies the capacity of a feedback capacitor, altering the frequency of the master oscillator. The direction of the change corrects any discrepancy between the vertical output and the 60-cps AC line. Disconnecting the "line-lock" link causes the master oscillator to operate as a free-running oscillator.

Phase difference between the AC line and the 60-cps vertical output stage (Q227 in Fig. 11-27) is detected in a dual discrimin-

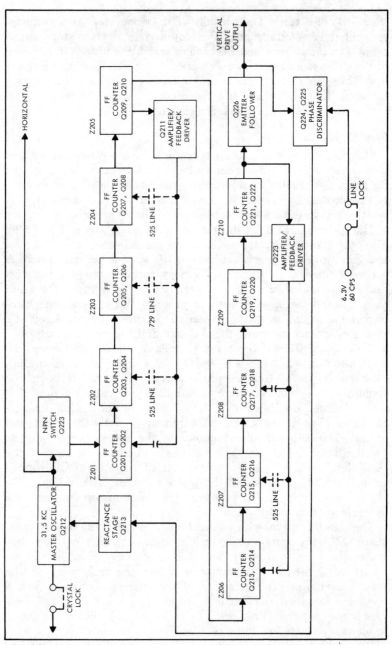

Courtesy Cohu/KinTel Electronics

Fig. 11-26. Block diagram of the sync-generator board used with a transistorized camera.

ator stage (Q226 and Q225). This type of AFC circuit has the advantage of transistor gain that is not available in normal diode AFC circuits. This gain permits a greater lock-in range.

The DC output of the discriminator is a function of the relative phases and frequencies of the two signals: the pulse from the 60-cps vertical output stage (Q227) and the 60-cps sine wave from the power line. When this pulse waveform coincides with the power line frequency, no voltage is applied to the master oscillator through reactance stage Q213. Any deviation in frequency or phase, however, causes an error voltage to develop in some direction.

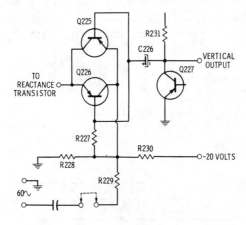

Fig. 11-27. Schematic of the phase detector circuit.

In Fig. 11-27 resistors R228 and R230 set the developed voltage reference for the base operation of the discriminator. The vertical output pulse waveform and the 60-cps power-line frequency are applied simultaneously to both transistor bases. The effect of any phase or frequency difference is such that the oscillator may "speed up" or "slow down" to restore coincidence.

A transistor switching circuit, biased as a normally off PNP switch, is turned on when a sine-wave signal from the master oscillator is applied to the base of the transistor. The transistor conducts only on a negative portion of the sine wave. Phase inversion produces a 20-volt peak-to-peak positive pulse at the collector which is fed to the first of the binary counters.

Flip-flop binary counters are essentially the same as the flip-flops that divided the basic 31.5-kc frequency in the horizontal deflection circuit. It will be recalled that the output of the flip-flop is taken from only one side, indicating that a frequency division by two has taken place, i.e., the flip-flop requires two pulses to count once.

This pulse is fed to the steering diodes of the following stage, which divides this frequency again by two, etc. A frequency division of 31.5 kc by 2^{10} (10: the number of binary counters), however, does not yield the 60 cps required for vertical scan. In order to arrive at the 60-cps rate, the binary counters are divided into two groups of five each. The first group, by application of

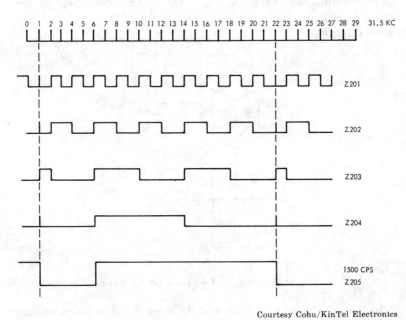

Courtesy Cohu/KinTel Electronics

Fig. 11-28. Pulse divisions accomplished by the first flip-flop binary counter group.

feedback pulses from a pulse amplifier/driver stage, is made to divide the crystal frequency by 21. The resultant frequency, 1,500 cps in the case of the 31.5-kc crystal, is then applied to the second group of five flip-flop binary counters.

The second group of five flip-flop binary counters is made to divide the resultant frequency by 25 to arrive at the 60-cps vertical rate. The top pulse waveform in Fig. 11-28 is the clock pulse rate. Note that the pulse waveform directly below it has a feedback or reset pulse every 21st cycle. This pulse resets the flip-flop and causes it, in this case, to miss every 21st pulse by resetting the flip-flop. The second and fourth pulse waveforms also show the effects of a feedback pulse. The third and fifth flip-flop counters do not receive a feedback pulse. The second group of five flip-flops

(Fig. 11-29) operates in the same manner as the first group except that the division by the entire group is by 25. It should be noted that the length and amplitude of the feedback pulse is only large enough to cause the flip-flop and multivibrators to reset.

Pulse amplifier/feedback drivers Q211 and Q223 (Fig. 11-26) are straight grounded-emitter amplifiers utilized in driving stages. The input pulse is amplified and used to reset the predetermined

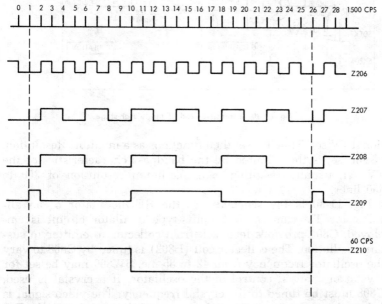

Courtesy Cohu/KinTel Electronics

Fig. 11-29. Pulse divisions accomplished by the second flip-flop binary counter group.

flip-flop binary counters required to yield the desired count. Vertical output transistor Q227 (Fig. 11-27) is also a grounded-emitter amplifier used as a driver. The 60-cps vertical-input pulse is amplified and applied to the deflection circuit board. The power supplies for this camera are voltage-regulated, an important requirement for successful camera performance in many closed-circuit TV systems that are required to operate continuously.

RF Modulator

With the addition of a signal generator operating at the same frequencies as commercial TV channels, and by applying modulation at a video frequency, it is possible to connect the output of a video-frequency camera to the antenna terminals of a conven-

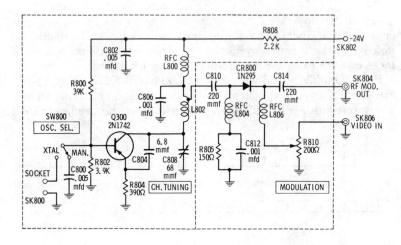

Fig. 11-30. A transistorized RF modulator stage.

tional TV set. That TV set then functions as a monitor. Resolution, of course, is then limited by the bandpass characteristics of the TV set, usually resulting in a maximum resolution of 300 to 350 lines.

Fig. 11-30 is the schematic of the RF modulator of an all-transistor TV camera. A Colpitts-type oscillator circuit is employed. C804 provides feedback from collector to emitter to sustain oscillation. The collector coil (L802) is tuned by C808 to vary the oscillator frequency from 42 to 85 mc. SW800 may be set for crystal or manual control of the oscillator. If a crystal is used, C808 must be tuned to the crystal frequency. The video signal is fed to the cathode of a 1N295 crystal diode modulator; the RF signal is coupled to the anode. R810 is the modulation level adjustment.

VIDEO DISTRIBUTION/LINE AMPLIFIER

Distribution or line amplifiers are used to maintain signal levels and signal-to-noise ratios at their proper level. They compensate for losses in amplitude levels introduced by passive equipment in the system. The simplified block diagram of a typical distribution amplifier is given in Fig. 11-31. A single video source, such as a TV camera, either composite or noncomposite, is connected to the input of the unit. Output connections for feeding up to three separate distribution cables are provided for use as a distribution amplifier. When they are used as an amplifier feeding a single output cable, the two unused output connections must be terminated to maintain the uniform, wideband frequency response capability of the amplifier: ±0.25 db to 8 mc, ±1.0 db to 10 mc. A control enables the gain of the amplifier to be varied from unity to a maximum of 11 db for boosting low-level signals to a standard distribution level before the signals are fed to a transmission line, monitor, recorder, or the system.

Two wideband video amplifiers in cascade connection form the signal circuit of the amplifier. Two coaxial input receptacles are provided for looping the signal through the amplifier input or for terminating the input line with a resistive load to match the low impedance of the coaxial cable to which it may be connected. The first amplifier stage has a gain of 11 db and feeds the gain control as its output load. The gain control is adjustable over a range of 12 db. The second stage of the video amplifier has essentially unity gain and drives three outputs through isolation resistors. The isolation resistors in conjunction with the inherently low impedance of the output of the amplifier provide isolation between the output signals. This isolation prevents any disturbance on one line from affecting the signals on either of the other two lines. Because of this arrangement, an open or shorted circuit on any one of the lines will not cause the amplifier to become inoperative. A feedback loop in the amplifier serves to provide gain stability despite changes in tube characteristics with age. The power supply is voltage regulated to assure stable output signal levels over wide variations in power line voltages.

EQUIPMENT MAINTAINANCE

A regular schedule of inspection and maintenance should be established to avoid catastrophic failures and to reduce the possibility of interruptions in service. Periodic inspections of all

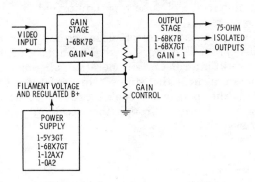

Fig. 11-31. Block diagram of the RCA MI-36315 distribution amplifier.

units in the system should be made to assure that dust and dirt that may collect in the enclosures are thoroughly cleaned out. The accumulation of dust and moisture can result in excessive leakage and probable arc-over between high-voltage points. All cable connections should be periodically inspected. Any signs of oxidation should be carefully removed. All ground straps and connectors should be examined to assure secure contacts.

A record of performance and operating data should be kept for each unit of equipment. The records should be examined during the maintenance periods as a reference that will immediately indicate any deterioration or deviations from normal performance. Instruction manuals supplied with the equipment should be filed and referred to during maintenance checks to assure that specifications for performance are continuously complied with, and, when making adjustments, that the manufacturers' recommendations are followed. A schedule of maintenance should follow this typical pattern:

Daily: Check knob positions to note any deviations from the usual settings. Check picture quality.

Weekly: Clean equipment internally and externally. Check power supplies for voltages and regulation. Measure voltage drops across filter circuits in power supplies to determine if normal load currents have changed. If any changes have developed, they are an indication of trouble and indicate the need for troubleshooting.

Monthly: In addition to the *daily* and *weekly* checks, the monthly check should include a test of all tubes in the system with comparisons made of all previously recorded readings for all individual tubes. This will give an indication of potential tube trouble and is one of the most effective methods for preventive maintenance of tube-type equipment.

The leading manufacturers of closed-circuit television equipment usually provide comprehensive manuals for their units. These give useful information in operation, alignment, and maintenance. There is a cliche that states, "No one besides the man who wrote it reads the instruction book." Prove it is wrong in your case, and you will profit through the excellent performance of your CCTV system.

APPENDIX A

Glossary

A

Aberration—In an optical lens, a defect that does not bring all the light rays transmitted by the lens to the same point of focus. In a cathode-ray tube, a defect when the electron lens does not bring the electron beam to the same point of sharp focus at all points on the screen.

Anode—The positive electrode of a vacuum tube; also called the plate.

Aperture—An opening that permits light, electrons, or other forms of radiation to pass. In an electron gun, the aperture determines the size and has an effect on the shape of the electron beam. In television optics, it is the effective diameter of the lens that controls the amount of light reaching the surface of the vidicon target.

Aspect ratio—The ratio of width to height for the frame of the televised picture. The U.S. standard is 4:3.

B

Balop—Contraction of balopticon, an apparatus for the projection of opaque images in conjunction with a television camera.

Bandwidth—The width of a band of frequencies. An "8-megacycle" bandwidth means that there is an 8-mc difference between the highest and the lowest frequencies capable of being controlled, attenuated, or amplified by a unit of equipment.

271

Band-elimination filter—A device that attenuates a specific bandwidth of frequencies, also called a band-rejection filter.

Bandpass filter—The opposite of band-elimination filter. A bandpass filter will pass only a specific band of frequencies.

Barrel distortion—In television, distortion that makes the televised image appear to bulge outward on all sides like a barrel.

Beam—A concentrated, unidirectional flow of electrons or other energy.

Beam width—The angular width of a beam, measured in azimuth.

Black level—The level of a television picture signal that corresponds to the maximum limits of the black component of the picture.

Black negative—The television picture signal in which the polarity of the voltage corresponding to black is negative with respect to that which corresponds to the white area of the picture signal.

Blanking—The process of cutting off the electron beam in a vidicon or picture tube during the retrace period.

Blooming—An enlargement of the effective diameter of an electron beam that causes a halation and defocusing around bright areas on the monitor screen.

Bridging—Connecting two electrical circuits in parallel.

Bridging amplifier—An amplifier for bridging an electrical circuit without introducing an apparent change in the performance of that circuit.

Burn—In a vidicon, a burn is the sticking or persistence of an image in the output signal of a television camera which is visible on the monitor screen after the camera has been turned away from the image. In a picture tube it is a blemish or localized discoloration of the screen.

C

Camera chain—A television camera, associated control units, power supplies, monitor, and connecting cables.

Camera tube—Also called a pickup tube and a television camera tube.

Candlepower—Light intensity expressed in candles.

Cathode—The negative electrode of a vacuum tube.

Cathode-ray tube—Also called CRT and kinescope; a tube in which the electrons emitted by a heated cathode are focused into a beam and directed toward a phosphor-coated surface which then becomes luminescent at the point where the electron beam strikes it.

Coaxial cable—A conductor centered inside of and insulated from a cylinder which is also used as a conductor. The two conductors are separated by a dielectric.

Coma—A defect in a cathode-ray tube that makes the normally circular electron beam appear comet shaped at the edges of the tube screen.

Community antenna television—Abbreviated to CATV, a television system that receives and retransmits commercial television broadcasts. Microwave transmitters and coaxial cables are used to bring the television signals to subscribers in a community.

Compatible—The ability of two systems, or two units of equipment, to integrate their capabilities.

Composite video signal—The combined signals in a television transmission, including the picture signal, vertical and horizontal blanking, and synchronizing signals.

Contrast—The difference in tone between white and black areas in a television picture.

Contrast range—The ratio between the whitest and blackest portions of a television image.

D

Dark current—The current that flows in a photoconductor when it is placed in total darkness.

Definition—The fidelity of a television system to the original scene.

Depth of field—The in-focus range of an optical system; it is measured from the distance behind an object to the distance ahead of the object when a viewing lens shows the object to be at the point of maximum focus.

E

Echo—A reflection of a transmitted television picture, appearing as a "ghost" on the screen of the monitor.

Electrostatic focusing—A method of focusing the cathode-ray beam to a fine spot.

Equalizer—A circuit configuration of electronic components that introduces compensation for frequency discriminative effects of elements within the television system.

F

Fade—To change signal strength.

Fade in—To increase signal strength gradually. Opposite of "fade out."

Fade out—To decrease signal strength gradually. Opposite of "fade in."

Fader—A control or group of controls for effecting fade in and fade-out of video or audio signals.

Field—One of the two equal parts into which a television frame is divided in an interlaced system of scanning.

Field frequency—The number of fields transmitted per second in a television system. The U.S. standard is 60 fields per second. Also called field-repetition rate.

Flip-flop circuit—A multivibrator circuit used in television to provide periodic pulses.

Focus—The point at which light rays or an electron beam form a minimum-size spot. Also the action of bringing light or electron beams to a fine spot.

Focus control—A manual adjustment for bringing the electron beam of a vidicon or picture tube to a minimum-size spot, producing the sharpest image.

Footcandle—A unit of illuminance, incident light.

Footlambert—A unit of luminance, emitted or reflected light.

Frame—The complete television image.

Front projection—A system of picture enlargement, using an opaque, reflective screen. The projector and viewers are on the same side of the screen.

G

Gamma—The numerical value of the degree of contrast in a television picture.

Gc—Abbreviation for gigacycle (1 billion cycles); also called kilomegacycle.

Ghost image—Undesirable duplication on the monitor screen of the image.

H

Halation—A glow or diffusion that surrounds a bright spot on a television picture tube screen. A defect in quality is indicated.

High-contrast image—A picture in which strong contrast between light and dark areas is visible. Intermediate values, however, may be missing.

High definition—The television equivalent of high fidelity.

Highlight—Bright area in a television scene.

Horizontal blanking—Blanking of the picture during the period of horizontal retrace.

Horizontal resolution—The number of individual picture elements that can be distinguished in a horizontal scanning line; also called horizontal definition.

I

Iconoscope—A type of television camera tube.

Image orthicon—A type of television camera tube. It is popular in commercial-television station applications.

Incident light—The light that falls directly on an object.

Interlaced scanning—A technique for reducing image flicker in a television image. The odd- and even-numbered lines are transmitted consecutively as two separate fields.

Isolation amplifier—An amplifier with input circuitry and output circuitry designed to eliminate the effects of changes made at either upon the other.

J

Jack—A connector into which a plug may be inserted or removed at will.

Jeep—Modification of a television receiver intended for RF systems so that a VF signal can be connected.

Jitter—Lack of steadiness in the interlace.

K

Kinescope—A cathode-ray or picture tube.

Kinescope recording—A recording on motion-picture film made by photographing the image on a picture-tube screen.

L

Line amplifier—An amplifier for audio or video signals that feeds a transmission line; also called program amplifier.

Line of sight—The shortest distance or optical path between two objects. The distance to the horizon from an elevated point.

Load—That which receives the output of a unit of equipment.

Loss—Power dissipation that serves no useful purpose.

M

Moire—A pattern of converging lines visible on the screen of a monitor picture tube. It results from spurious interference.

Monitor—A unit of equipment that displays (on the face of a picture tube) the images detected and transmitted by a television camera.

Monitor amplifier—A unit of equipment intended for amplifying audio signals for the purpose of monitoring the signals fed to the distribution system.

Monostable—Having only one stable state.

N

NAB—Abbreviation for National Association of Broadcasters.

NARTB—Abbreviation for National Association of Radio and Television Broadcasters. Now the NAB.

NTSC—Abbreviation for National Television System Committee which established the standards for black and white and color television.

O

Optical axis—The straight line passing through the centers of the curved surfaces of a lens.

P

Pairing—A faulty interlace scan wherein the alternate scanning lines tend to overlap each other. The effect is a severe reduction in vertical resolution capability.

Passive—Incapable of generating power or amplification.

Patchboard—A panel containing a number of jacks and terminations.

Peak-to-peak voltage—The sum of the extreme negative and positive alternations of a signal.

Persistence—The period of time a phosphor continues to glow after the excitation source is removed.

Photoconductor—A device whose electrical resistance varies in relationship with exposure to light.

Pickup tube—A camera tube.

Picture size—The useful area of a picture tube.

Picture tube—The cathode-ray tube in a monitor on which the picture is displayed.

Pin-cushion distortion—Distortion in a television picture that makes all sides appear to bulge inward.

Plug—The mating connector for a jack.

R

Random interlace—A technique for scanning that is often used in closed-circuit television systems. It offers somewhat reduced precision to that employed in commercial broadcast service.

Raster—The area of a picture tube scanned by the electron beam.

Resolution—A measure of the ability of a unit or a complete television system to delineate detail between two quantities of equal value.

Rolloff—A gradual increase in attenuation of a signal voltage.

S

Sawtooth waveform—Resembling the teeth of a saw, such a waveform has a slow or sloping rise time, and a sharp or sudden fallback to the starting point.

Scanning—Moving the electron beam of a pickup tube or a picture tube diagonally across the target or screen area of tube.

Schmidt system—A system of optics used in many TV projectors.

Sync—A contraction of synchronous or synchronization.

T

Talk-back—A voice intercommunicator, an intercom.

Test pattern—A chart especially prepared for checking overall performance of a television system. It contains various combinations of lines and geometric shapes. The camera is focused on the chart, and the pattern is viewed at the monitor for fidelity.

V

Vertical resolution—Same as vertical definition. The number of horizontal lines that can be seen in the reproduced image of a television pattern.

Vertical retrace—The return of the electron beam to the top of the picture tube screen or the pickup tube target at the completion of the field scan.

Video—Picture.

Video amplifier—A wideband amplifier for the picture signals.

Video signal—The picture signal. A signal containing visual information, as well as blanking and synchronizing pulses in a television system.

Vidicon—One type of television camera tube. It is especially popular in closed-circuit television applications.

Voltage amplifier—A unit of equipment that builds up the value of a voltage.

W

Waveform monitor—An oscilloscope designed especially for viewing the waveform of a video signal.

Z

Zoom—To enlarge or reduce on a continuously variable basis the size of a televised image. It may be done electronically or optically.

APPENDIX B

Sources of Supply

In planning a closed-circuit television system it is useful to contact the manufacturers of equipment considered essential. Usually, the literature prepared by suppliers contains general information on closed-circuit television, in addition to data and descriptions of their own products. Some manufacturers make their equipment available through distributors who provide assistance in planning, specifying, installing, and servicing the products. Therefore, when contacting a manufacturer, it is suggested that you ask about local sources of supply and service. Other manufacturers provide field engineering assistance through branch offices or direct from the factories; charges for such services are sometimes not made, or they may be included in the quotation for a system.

As with all sources of supply, it is virtually impossible to prepare a list that is complete. The very nature of business, especially one with a growth factor such as is being experienced by the closed-circuit television business, indicates the frequent appearance (and disappearance) of new (and old) names on the roster of manufacturers. The author has made every effort to be complete and accurate. To the best of his knowledge, the sources given in the following table are accurate, up to date (1969), and complete. It is based entirely on queries made to known major manufacturers with national sales programs, and the replies they made to these queries. The numbers alongside the manufacturer listings give the categories of products each offers. The key to the numbers is given at the end of the listings.

SOURCE

Adler Electronics, Inc.   13
1 LeFevre Lane
New Rochelle, New York 10801

Admiral Corp.   6, 14
Government Electronics Div.
3800 West Cortland Street
Chicago, Illinois 60647

Alpha Wire Corp.   7
200 Varick Street
New York, N. Y. 10014

American Communications Corp.   10
280 Broadway
New York, N. Y. 10007

American Microwave & TV Corp.   4
1369 Industrial Road
San Carlos, California 94070

Ampex Corp.   4, 14, 25
401 Broadway
Redwood City, California 94063

Belden Manufacturing Co.   7
415 S. Kilpatrick Avenue
Chicago, Illinois 60644

Bell Television, Inc.   6
552 West 53rd Street
New York, N. Y. 10019

Bendix Corp.   6
Communications Div.
East Joppa Road
Baltimore, Maryland 21204

Cohu Electronics, Inc.   4, 6, 11
KinTel Div.
Box 623
San Diego, California 92112

Conrac Div.   14
Giannini Controls Corp.
Glendora, California 91740

Continental Electronics   4
Box 17040
Dallas, Texas 75217

SOURCE

Dage–Bell Div.   3, 4, 6, 9, 13, 19, 19
Subsidiary of the Raytheon Co.
455 Sheridan Avenue
Michigan City, Indiana 46403

Davis & Sanford Co., Inc.   5, 15, 21
24 Pleasant Street
New Rochelle, New York 10801

Entron, Inc.   1
2141 Industrial Parkway
Silver Spring, Maryland 20904

Fairchild Camera & Instrument Co.   4
Dumont Electron Tubes Div.
750 Bloomfield Avenue
Clifton, New Jersey 07015

General Television Network   22
901 Livernois Avenue
Ferndale, Michigan 48220

GPL Div.   4, 6, 22, 24
General Precision, Inc.
63 Bedford Road
Pleasantville, New York 10570

Giantview Division   22
Meilink Steel Safe Co.
901 Livernois Avenue
Ferndale, Michigan

ITT   4
Industrial Products Div.
15191 Bledsoe Street
San Fernando, California 91342

Jerrold Electronics Corp.   1, 10, 12
The Jerrold Building
15th and Lehigh Avenue
Philadelphia, Pa. 19105

Lear Siegler, Inc.   4, 6
Electronic Instrumentation Div.
714 North Brookhurst Avenue
Anaheim, California 92801

Magnavox Co.   14
270 Park Avenue
New York, N. Y. 10017

SOURCE

Micro-Link Div. Varian Associates 75 Akron St., Dept. T Copiague, New York 11726	13
Miratel Electronics, Inc. 3601 Richardson Street St. Paul, Minnesota 55112	14
Motorola Communications & Electronics, Inc. 4501 W. Augusta Blvd. Chicago, Illinois 60651	14
Packard-Bell Electronics Corp. 1920 South Figueroa Street Los Angeles, California 90007	4, 14
Pelco Sales, Inc. 351 E. Alondra Blvd. Gardena, California 90247	11, 17
Precision Instrument Co. 3170 Porter Drive Palo Alto, California 94304	25
Quick-Set, Inc. 8121 Central Park Avenue Skokie, Illinois 60078	5, 21
Radio Corp. of America Broadcast & Communications Prod. Div. Front and Cooper Street Camden, New Jersey 08102	1, 2, 3, 4, 5, 6, 9, 10, 13, 14, 15, 16, 18, 19, 20, 21, 23, 24, 25
Sarkes-Tarzian, Inc. Broadcast Equipment Div. East Hillside Drive Bloomington, Indiana 47401	1, 2, 3, 4, 5, 6, 9, 10, 13, 18, 19, 23
Stereotronics Corp. 1717 North Highland Street Los Angeles, California 90028	20
Sylvania Electric Products, Inc. 730 Third Avenue New York, N. Y. 10017	4, 6, 14, 21
Tele-Measurements, Inc. 45 West 45th Street New York, N. Y. 10036	22

SOURCE

Vue-Tronics, Inc. 920 North Citrus Avenue Los Angeles, California 90038	24
Weatherscan R. H. Tyler Co. 1410 Dallas Street Wellington, Texas 79095	6
Westbury CATV Corp. 4 Tecumseh Avenue Mt. Vernon, New York 10553	1, 10
Zoomar, Inc. 55 Sea Cliff Avenue Glen Cove, New York 11542	26

CODE	PRODUCT CATEGORY
1	Amplifiers (audio, equalizer, RF, video-bridging, cue, distribution, isolation, line, program, talk-back).
2	Audio consoles.
3	Cabinets (racks and consoles).
4	Cameras.
5	Camera mounts.
6	CCTV systems (special application setups for commerce, industry, military, research, science).
7	Coaxial cable and wire materials.
8	ETV consoles (mobile, self contained).
9	Faders.
10	Hardware for CCTV.
11	Housings (environmental).
12	Master antenna systems.
13	Microwave equipment.
14	Monitors.
15	Monitor mounts.
16	Multiplexers.
17	Pan/tilt heads (remote control, electric).
18	Switchers.
19	Sync generators.
20	Three-D TV optics.
21	Tripods and dollies.
22	TV projection equipment.
23	Video consoles.
24	Video film recorders (kinescope systems).
25	Video tape recorders.
26	Zoom lenses (remote control, electric).

Index